The Schoolhouse Burned Twice

by BENT AXEL LARSEN

PACIFIC PRESS PUBLISHING ASSOCIATION
Mountain View, California   Omaha, Nebraska

cover and illustrations by VERNON NYE

This is a true story about real people I have
known; but I have changed some of the
names of persons and places.   —B.A.L.

Contents

Mamani, Jacinto, and Juana traveled through tough yellow
grass of the high plateau, on their way to the gay "fiesta."

Feast Day 1

Sergio Mamani jogged along on his burro, urging it through the tough yellow grass of the two-mile-high plateau. Cold wind blew his poncho, and white clouds whipped across the bright sky. He saw the icy rivers winding through the valleys below, flowing toward the great Lake Titicaca. The steep cliffs of the Andean mountains of Peru towered above him.

The last two days had been exciting. Early yesterday morning Mamani had taken his wife and son to Santiago, the town nearest their own tiny village. There they had joined hundreds of others in celebrating the *fiesta de Santiago* (feast of Saint James). They ate, drank, sang, and danced as though each person were trying to outdo the other in honoring Santiago, patron saint of their town.

Mamani had not slept all night. But not until now as he was returning home had he felt his tiredness. He glanced at his six-year-old son Jacinto, who sat in front of him on the burro.

The boy must be tired too, Mamani thought.

Juana, Mamani's wife, trotted beside the burro, carrying a heavy bundle on her back and faithfully spinning brown llama wool into yarn. He noticed her shift the bundle to a higher position.

"So she's tired too," he thought. "Well, what if we are tired? It was a good *fiesta*."

In his mind Mamani could still hear the high, shrill music of the flutes and the monotonous pounding of the drums that had drowned the other sounds of the *fiesta*, even the giddy screams of the women and the laughter of the men. When he closed his eyes, he could almost see the proud men and women circling and swaying in time to the music. He remembered how he and Juana had joined the dancers, and even little Jacinto had gotten into the act by stamping a few simple steps.

5

Now Jacinto interrupted Mamani's thoughts.

"Wasn't Santiago beautiful? Wasn't he wonderful?" Jacinto asked.

Mamani knew his son had been much impressed when certain specially chosen men had carried the statue of Santiago in a procession through the streets.

"When I grow up to be a strong man, I would like to be one of those who carry Santiago on the day of the *fiesta*. May I, Papa?"

"Yes, you may," said Mamani, "but only if you become as strong and loyal to the Virgin Mary as Santiago."

"Santiago must have been a strong apostle," Jacinto said, and his eyes glittered with enthusiasm.

Mamani had great dreams for Jacinto. He hoped his son would become far greater than a saint bearer. Yet he rejoiced that the boy took interest in the religious part of the holiday. Mamani hoped his son would feel as devoted to the church as he had always felt. For while Mamani was a popular leader in the drinking and dancing, he still took time to worship the saints, and he attended mass every Sunday morning.

Mamani rode on silently, watching the yellow grass blow in the wind. Somehow the good feeling had left him now. His head felt heavy, and his heart felt empty. He thought about the mestizos, people who are a half-breed mixture of Spanish and Indian. Most of the well-to-do people in Santiago were mestizos. Why had they laughed at him as he danced? Why didn't they dance behind him like the Indians? He knew that the townspeople believed in the saint and that they liked to dance and get drunk. Why didn't they drink with the Indians during the *fiesta* instead of keeping to themselves and dressing differently? How was it that they had the privilege of learning to read and write and he did not? None of his Indian friends could read or write. But he knew that almost all the mestizos learned these things.

Mamani pushed the lump of coca leaves from his cheek to the center of his mouth and spat it out, wiping the green spit from his lips with a tip of his poncho. He had often tried to quit the coca-chewing habit, but every time he came right back to using it. Coca seemed to give him strength.

6

"Why is it that the mestizos never use coca?" asked Jacinto. He seemed to be reading his father's thoughts.

"Coca is for the workingman," Mamani explained. "The mestizos do not work as hard as we poor Indians do. They can get along without coca. But we need the strength it gives. Then, too, the mestizos prefer smoking the cigarette."

The burro poked along. "*Anda* [move along]!" shouted Mamani as he kicked his heels into the sides of the animal. The burro took a few faster steps but soon fell back into his normal slow pace. Juana also walked a little faster. She was perspiring, and she pushed her bundle with a jerk still higher up on her back, and she bent lower under the weight. The afternoon sun felt warm. Mamani felt hot on the side where the sun shone, but the leg on the shady side of the burro was cold. Little Jacinto drowsed. In the distance a dust cloud indicated the approach of a *caballero*.

"*El patrón* [The landlord] is coming," Mamani said. "It is Señor González."

Señor González owned the best land around Condorrumi, Sergio Mamani's home village. A big, heavyset man of Spanish descent, he had a round, rosy face and a heavy black moustache. Today as always he wore a wide-brimmed hat, riding pants, and boots with big silver spurs. As he came near Mamani's family, he slowed down. Mamani, Jacinto, and Juana greeted him in Quechua, their Indian language.

"*Tayta, tayta,*" they said.

Then Mamani surprised the *caballero* by adding a Spanish greeting. Mamani had never done this before. But he had learned a little Spanish and was trying to teach Jacinto a few words.

"*Buenas tardes,* Señor González [Good afternoon, Mr. Gonzáles]," he said politely, bowing his head toward the *patrón*. And little Jacinto repeated respectfully, "*Buenas tardes,* señor."

Señor González jerked his horse to a stop. His face twisted into a snarl.

"Who do you think you are?" he asked. "How dare you salute me in this way? Spanish is not your language. I have always spoken to you in Quechua, and I want you to salute me as you have always done. Do you understand?"

7

The Schoolhouse Burned Twice

"Allinchu [All right]," Mamani said and again bowed his head.

"Bueno [Good]. Remember you are just an Indian." Then Señor González swore and planted the spurs deep in the sides of his horse.

As the animal started forward, the *caballero* turned toward Mamani and mumbled, "You dead dog! Piece of a louse!"

Mamani looked back as the man disappeared in a cloud of dust and wondered why Señor González had become so angry. González had been a hard and severe *patrón,* but Mamani had always gotten along fine with him. Today he had only wanted to be especially nice by speaking in the great man's own language. Why should be resent being greeted in Spanish? He had always greeted Mamani in the Indian language, Quechua. Why couldn't Mamani greet González in *his* language? After all, Spanish was the official language of Peru.

All the way home Mamani continued to ask himself these questions. Could it be, he wondered, that Señor González and the rest of the townspeople hated to see the Indians rise from ignorance to knowledge? He was just as much a Peruvian as Señor González, Mamani told himself. Was being born an Indian reason enough to keep him ignorant about his rights as a citizen, his government, and his country? Was reading and writing only for the white man or mestizo? No, he knew that his government wanted schools for children of all the people. How he wished Jacinto could go to school and learn to read books and newspapers about the great world that seemed so distant and strange!

Mamani's back ached. His head hurt. Every step the burro took jarred the bones along his spine. Juana drooped with weariness and had stopped spinning wool. The full spindle stuck out from the top of the bundle on her back.

At last the travelers came into view of the hills of Condorrumi. Mamani could see the great rock just above the village where the old folk claimed that a condor used to nest. That was why they had named the village Condorrumi.

"Look, Papa, there is our home," Jacinto said, pointing toward the place where their own little house and the houses of their neighbors nestled among rocks at the foot of the hills.

Mamani loved Condorrumi. He loved his animals and the blessed earth which gave daily nourishment to his family. His small fields lay at the base of the hills, and above them ripe barley fields looked like yellow patches on the mountainside. Before Condorrumi, in the middle of the valley, flowed the river bordered by the fertile pastures of the *patrón,* Señor González.

When the family reached home, Mamani lifted the saddle from his burro and hung it on a wall while Jacinto set the animal loose in the corral. Then Mamani sat down on the bench in front of the long section of his compound, the section where he and his family slept and spent their free hours after dark. He was facing the empty patio. How different it looked during those frequent evenings when men of the village gathered there to discuss problems. To Mamani's left lay the kitchen hut, and he could hear Juana inside clattering clay bowls and her big pots as she began supper. White smoke from the cook fire seeped through the straw of the kitchen roof. The muttering sounds of the llamas and goats herded into the building that made the third side of his compound told him they wanted to be fed. But for the time being he paid no attention.

Instead, Mamani's eyes rested on his son, who played on the low adobe wall across the front of his patio. Tiredness had already deserted the boy as he straddled the wall, pretending it to be a horse. Mamani heard the plaintive tones of a flute song, and his eyes roamed past Jacinto and the wall to the green pastures of Señor González in the valley. Several geese ambled peacefully with a flock of sheep which a young shepherd boy guided along the homeward path. As the boy walked he played a melancholy tune on his flute, and the song deepened the sadness Mamani felt since meeting Señor González on the way home. Usually Mamani loved the flute music, but tonight its melody seemed to cry to him with all the hopeless longing of his people. Would they never be considered as good as the mestizos? Was Jacinto doomed to the same ignorance and poverty his ancestors had always known?

Mamani glanced back at Jacinto and saw that he now pretended to be Santiago. Still straddling the wall as though it were a horse, he held a stick high in his right hand like a sword and looked

9

straight forward in imitation of the saint. He hummed the rythmic dance music he had heard at the *fiesta*.

Now Jacinto came to sit next to his father on the bench.

"Papa, why was it that Santiago had a broken arm? Did you see how it was mended and glued together?"

"Yes, I know," said Mamani. "Last year at the *fiesta*, Santiago had an accident. He fell and broke his arm."

Jacinto was thoughtful for a long time, and his father hoped he would ask no more questions about the saint's broken arm. The year before, the people had quarreled with the local priest over the price of the mass to be said during the *fiesta*. *El Padre* Medrano, who had come from Spain, was friendly and likable; but he was very zealous for the dignity of his office and parish.

"No pay, no saint," he had said. "If you do not pay for the mass in advance, there will be no procession with Santiago at the *fiesta*."

The representatives from the neighboring communities had much respect for their priest, but the price he wanted had simply been too high for them. They refused to pay it, and the priest refused to say mass or allow the statue of Santiago to be used in the procession. The people missed the traditional procession, and as the drinking proceeded the first night of the *fiesta*, they decided to take the statue out anyway. They broke into the church and, in spite of the padre's protest, brought the saint out in procession, dragging along with them *el Padre* Medrano, who stubbornly held on to the saint. In the commotion and the drunken turmoil, the statue had fallen from its platform to the hard ground of the church plaza. The uplifted arm with the sword had broken off. This had seemed a tragedy to the people. Many devout women shed tears as they looked at the shattered arm lying on the ground, and the men became suddenly sober as with scarcely a word they scooped up the broken arm and carried the statue silently back inside the church.

Finally Jacinto broke the silence. "Papa," he said, "Santiago is not so great a saint after all, is he?"

"Why not?"

"If he was so great a hero and a real saint, wouldn't God have protected him? If he can help and lead the cavalry to victory in battle, why couldn't he keep himself from falling?"

Mamani had asked himself these questions many times, so he found it difficult to answer. "You see, Jacinto, it is not the real saint. You know it is just an *imagen* of the real Santiago. But Mamma is calling us now; let us go and have supper."

The Strange Visitor   2

On a warm afternoon in November when summer seemed to have returned to stay, the weather suddenly changed. A cold wind tore through the valley, and black clouds gathered in the east promising thunder and rain. Then the first flash of lightning split the dark sky.

Mamani, who had just come home from his field, looked up between the houses toward the threatening clouds. As he searched the sky above the hills, he noticed two men walking down the hill that led from Huaquillo, a neighboring village. One of them carried a heavy pair of saddlebags over his shoulder and a small satchel in his hand.

Mamani hurried to get a few things under shelter to protect them from the threatening rain, wondering who the two strangers could be. His tangle-haired dog started growling, and then with vicious barking set out to meet the visitors. He seemed determined not to let any strangers come near the house. But the man with the saddlebags did not seem afraid. He kept the dog at a distance with a stick while he greeted Mamani with a smile. Then he let the saddlebags down on the mud bench.

"Where is your companion?" Mamani asked.

"My companion! I do not have any companion. I came all alone from Huaquillo."

"That certainly is queer," Mamani said. "I am sure I saw a strong man with you. He walked by your side but did not carry anything."

The stranger smiled again. "Well, I don't know what you saw. But one thing I do know, the angel of God is always with me. Maybe you saw him."

Mamani's wonder grew to amazement. The stranger really seemed to believe what he said.

"He did not look like an angel to me, although he was tall and strong. But you certainly do need the protection of God in this weather. I know how dangerous it is to walk over the hills in a thunderstorm. Had the storm begun a few minutes earlier, you could easily have been struck down."

And as if heaven would prove what he said, another flash of lightning ripped the sky, and thunder cracked like a cannon shot nearby.

"You got here just in time. May I bid you welcome? My house is yours for shelter, and there will also be a plate of hot soup."

By now the rain fell heavily, and as the visitor thanked his host, they entered the house.

"You are not from this province. I can tell from your clothes."

"Right you are. I must introduce myself. My name is Celestino Villca, and I come from Juliaca, where my hometown is Caracoto."

Though it was only late afternoon, the darkness of the sky made it seem much later. Only a small amount of light came in the two windows of the room to which Mamani invited his visitor. The windows were small, just small enough so a man could not crawl through. They had no glass, but their wooden shutters were closed. From wall to wall on both sides of the room, platforms made of adobe and covered by sheepskins and Indian blankets provided beds for the family. Mamani and his guest sat down on the beds opposite each other. The rain beat hard on the straw roof. They talked about the weather and the harvest and about the fair in Pucara which both of them had visited not long before.

Mamani took out his little woven coca bag and put the fragrant green leaves one by one into his mouth.

"I bought it at the fair," he said, showing the bag. "It is well made. Won't you join me? Help yourself, and here is some lime to go with it."

"No, thank you. I do not use coca."

"No?" How could that be? Mamani wondered. An Indian who refused a treat of coca! "Maybe you prefer to smoke a cigarette? I am sorry I do not have one to offer you."

"Thank you, but don't worry. I have never smoked, and I do not intend ever to begin."

13

"But don't you know that coca is good for you? It is good for hunger, thirst, weariness, heat, and cold. And above all, it gives you strength for work."

"I do not think so," Villca smiled. "You think it gives you strength, but it doesn't."

"Oh, yes," Mamani assured him, "I know it does. I cannot work without it."

"Tell me," asked Villca, "when you are on the road and your burro goes too slow, how do you make him go faster?"

Mamani wondered what that had to do with coca. "I kick him," he said, "or whip him with a stick."

"Exactly. The burro runs faster; but you don't believe that the stick gives strength to the burro, do you?"

Mamani thought. He saw the point, but he did not answer.

"You see," continued Celestino Villca, "there is no food value in these few dry leaves. But the medicine, or the drug that is in them, kicks the stomach and whips the nerves so that one feels pepped up. But it does not give strength. On the contrary, it ruins your stomach and irritates your nerves." Villca paused and smiled at Mamani. "It is the same with coffee, which stirs up the heart so that it beats faster but does it no good. And how do you feel after a day of drinking at the *fiesta*? You are not stronger, are you? You can hardly work the next day."

There was a pause. Then Mamani nodded. "I guess you are right. I have thought about it, but never that way. I really thought coca was good for me, though maybe it is not. I know it is not good for my stomach." He put the hard black piece of lime back into the coca bag and closed it. "Then I suppose you will not accept a glass of *chicha*, the beer I made from corn, or even a cup of coffee?"

"You are right. Why should I, when it is not good for me?"

What a strange visitor! Mamani decided he had never met an Indian like this one. No coca, no coffee, no *chicha*!

"How can you enjoy dancing without liquor?"

"I do not dance."

This surprised Mamani still more. "You do not dance! What do you do when you go to the *fiesta*?"

"I don't go to the *fiesta*."

Now Mamani leaned forward and searched the visitor's face. "Where did you learn all these strange things? You did not get these ideas all by yourself."

"Oh, no," said Villca. "We are many who believe in the same healthy practices. I learned it at the Seventh-day Adventist mission in Juliaca. I went to school there for three years. I have learned to read and write and to sing many wonderful songs."

Out of his saddlebags he took several books. On top of them he put a black book with red sides, and then he opened another small book. "Listen," he said, *"Diosmiy munahua, bay munachuan."*

"But that is Quechua you are reading!" exclaimed Mamani. "Is Quechua also in books?"

"Yes, that is a song in Quechua. Just listen, *'Diosmiy munahua* —[God loves me—]' " Villca sang in a clear melodious voice, "God loves me. He saved me. And I repeat again, My God loves me."

Jacinto, who had been with Juana in the kitchen, heard the singing and peeped through the door opening. He came to stand in amazement before the interesting stranger.

"This is my son, Jacinto. I wish he could learn to sing like you," said Mamani.

"Hello, Jacinto." Celestino Villca patted the little one on the shoulder. "Surely you can learn to sing. I shall teach you right now."

Juana also came in, and Mamani introduced her.

"We will all sing together, 'God loves me.' " Villca spoke with enthusiasm.

"Oh, no, I cannot sing," said Mamani.

"Neither can I," Juana protested.

"We will see. At least you can all learn to repeat the words."

With a little patience and a lot of repetition, Villca soon taught Mamani and his family to sing the simple tune and words. Juana enjoyed it, and her eyes sparkled as she noticed how well little Jacinto did. They spent a pleasant evening with their visitor. After supper he sang for them again and taught them more songs. He also read to them from the black Book.

"It is the Bible," he explained, "the Word of God."

The Schoolhouse Burned Twice

Jacinto listened attentively to all that Villca read and spoke, then suddenly he interrupted, "Do you believe in Santiago?"

"I believe every word of Santiago. I certainly do," said Villca. "I shall read to you from the book that Santiago wrote."

"Did Santiago really write a book?" Mamani asked in surprise.

"Oh, yes, an epistle," said Villca; "and he wrote it expressly to all who are followers of Jesus Christ, as Santiago was."

"You know," he added, "there are some who show their faith by following the image of Santiago in a procession. But isn't it much better to show one's belief by listening to what Santiago has to say to us and to do what he tells us?" Then Villca began to read in the Quechua language:

" 'If any of you lack wisdom, let him ask of God, that giveth to all men liberally, and upbraideth not; and it shall be given him. But let him ask in faith, nothing wavering. For he that wavereth is like a wave of the sea driven with the wind and tossed.' 'Wherefore, my beloved brethren, let every man be swift to hear.' 'Be ye doers of the Word, and not hearers only, deceiving your own selves.' " James 1:5, 6, 19, 22.

"I want to be a doer of the Word of God," said Mamani, "but how can I? I cannot read the Bible and have no one to teach me. I do not even know the law of God which Santiago writes about."

"You and your neighbors must build a school and get a teacher. You must learn to read for yourself. Juana should learn to read, and especially little Jacinto should go to a Christian school."

Villca told how the villagers in many places in the provinces of Juliaca, Juli, and Pomata had built their own schools and secured teachers from the Adventist mission.

The visitor's words penetrated Mamani's heart. The night became morning before he and Villca were through talking and the family lay down to rest. Mamani could not sleep, thinking of all that the visitor had told and taught them. He felt a sweetness in his heart as the words and melody of the little song about the love of God rang like a bell in his soul. A great desire gripped him to know more about the will of God, more about His Word for the security of his family's salvation and his own. If he could only read the Bible for himself. How wonderful it would be if they

16

could have a school in Condorrumi! Yes, then at least Jacinto would have an opportunity.

Mamani felt sure that God would help him and his neighbors build a school. Celestino Villca had prayed such a good prayer before they retired. He had prayed for God's blessings over Mamani's family and for a Christian school in the community. Villca could not be other than a man sent from God.

Mamani thought of the two men he had seen come over the hill in the thunderstorm. He felt sure he had not been mistaken. Had God given him a sign? Could it be that an angel of God had really come with Villca? He kept thinking and thinking until his head ached.

He loved Santiago. He had worshiped him and believed in him from boyhood. And now—now Villca had read the holy law of God, the Ten Commandments, one of which said: "Thou shalt not make unto thee any graven image . . .: thou shalt not bow down thyself to them, nor serve them."

How could he stop worshiping Santiago? He could not understand; but somehow he felt sure that God would make it clear to him.

"My God loves me." The melody of the little song still sang in his heart.

Celestino Villca ate breakfast with them. Although he could not read himself, Mamani bought a Bible, a songbook, and another book from his new friend who called himself a literature evangelist.

"Won't you stay with us for another day?" Mamani begged. "I will call the neighbors together so that you can talk to all of them and tell them the many wonderful things you have told us."

Villca stayed, and that afternoon most of the villagers gathered in Mamani's patio. The men sat on the adobe bench that lined two sides of the patio, while the women filled every inch of space on the dirt floor in the middle.

Villca could not speak fluently, but he captured the attention and interest of everyone present as he told them in a simple way about the need and responsibility of establishing a school in Condorrumi. He told them how the villagers in other places had their own mission schools. He encouraged them by reading God's promises from the Bible, and he even taught them some of the simple choruses he had taught Mamani's family. The villagers had never sung together before. They didn't sing well now, but they enjoyed the new experience.

Then, as leader of the community, Mamani took over, and an animated discussion followed. Everyone wanted his children to learn to read and write, but some of the people expressed fear and doubt that they would be allowed to have a school.

"The mestizos will not let us," one man said.

Another said, "We will have to get a license, and who will give us one?"

"It is a different religion. The *evangelistas* do not believe in the virgin or the saints."

"We will have to consult *el Padre* Medrano."

"The leagues are far to Juliaca. Maybe the mission will not have a teacher for us."

And so they continued. Mamani could foresee difficulties. But on one thing the villagers could all agree—they wanted a school.

Good News in Azangaro 3

Little Jacinto stood on top of the low adobe wall in front of his father's house and waved at Villca, who walked down the road toward Azangaro. Mamani stood behind him, and Juana came to stand at her husband's side. He smiled at his wife and put his arm around her shoulder.

"Hasn't it been a wonderful visit?" Mamani said. "I hope that it will not have been in vain that God sent him to Condorrumi."

Villca turned and waved to his new friends.

"God bless him," said Juana. "I hope he will come back soon."

"His saddlebags are lighter now. He sold a good number of books yesterday after the meeting." Mamani turned while he continued resolutely, "Now I must call a meeting so that we can get the work started on our school building."

"Look, Papa, Celestino is going to the hacienda. How dare he? He is a brave man, isn't he, Daddy?" Celestino Villca was Jacinto's new hero.

A little way to the left from the road they could see the tall eucalyptus trees which surrounded the hacienda of Señor González. The whitewashed, two-story building looked quite imposing in comparison to the Indian homes.

Mamani's heart went out for Villca. He wondered how his friend would be received in the mansion, and he could tell that Juana worried too.

Little Jacinto sang in his childish voice, "God loves me. He saved me." And Juana hummed the tune as she began sweeping the patio.

"What a difference," Mamani thought, "between the dance tunes of the *fiesta* and those sweet words of the songs Villca taught us."

The Schoolhouse Burned Twice

The possibility of having a school gave the villagers a common interest as nothing else had done for years. That same afternoon they met again in Mamani's patio. The enthusiasm was great. Mamani donated land on which the school should be built, with space enough for a teacher's house and also for a large playground. In addition, he promised two hundred adobe bricks and a number of straight poles for the roof. Much leveling of the ground had to be done, much digging for the foundation, and the adobe bricks had to be made.

"I will give a day's work every week until the school is finished," promised one of the villagers.

"I will give two days a week if necessary," said another.

"I also." Several hands went up.

"I will make two hundred adobes."

"I will buy ten long poles for the roof."

"I will give the straw needed for the adobe," the potter said. And so they kept on. Everybody wanted to do something.

The work had to be done quickly, especially the adobe must be made and dried and stored securely before the rainy season which would begin in December.

The meeting had almost come to a close when Ambrosio, an Indian who worked on Señor González's farm, arrived at the patio. Ambrosio's red face showed that he loved the *copita* (wine cup) and that he was much addicted to coca. Looking around at the men, he sucked a mouthful of green juice from an enormous ball of coca in his right cheek and let it splash unashamed on the patio floor.

Then he turned to Mamani. "Do you know what happened to that *evangelista protestante* [Protestant preacher] who was here yesterday?"

Ambrosio had a spiteful tone in his high-pitched voice, and the emphasis he put on the word *protestante* plainly showed his dislike for the Adventist colporteur.

"No." Mamani sensed bad news. "I saw him go into the hacienda. What happened?"

"*El patrón* gave him a terrible beating and sent him off to jail." Ambrosio spat again and threw a scornful look at the men.

Mamani felt something falling inside of him. Villca in jail! He could not believe it. Wouldn't God protect him?

"How do you know?"

"I saw it with my own eyes. I was right there in the patio when Villca talked to the wife, Doña Teresa. She was kind to *el evangelista*, and bought a book for the children and a Bible, but he had to promise not to tell anyone. She was afraid, you know. Such books are prohibited for Catholics. She crossed herself several times and was just getting the money to pay for the books, when González rode in through the gate with the overseer.

"You should have heard Señor González when he saw the *protestante!* He spieled off a long string of oaths, and Doña Teresa fled with her children inside the house. He roared at Villca something terrible and called him *diablo evangelista* and a thief who sneaked around on other people's properties. Villca tried to explain and to protest, but *el patrón* told him to get out quick. He was really mad. 'Beat him,' he said to the overseer. 'A good whipping will get him going.'

"Well, you all know how cruel the overseer is. He really gave it to *el protestante*. He turned his horse, lifted his horsewhip, and brought it down across Villca's back. Poor man, he had to run as fast as he could, while the overseer kept on beating him. Even when he stumbled and fell over the dogs that rushed at him, he had to endure more blows until González called a stop and told the overseer to take Villca to the police station to be locked up 'for a good long time.'" Ambrosio licked his lip in satisfaction as he watched the surprised expressions on the faces of his audience.

"So that is where Villca is," he continued—"in the *calabozo* {jail}, and good for him. Maybe he will stay away now. Who wants the *evangelistas* around here? They think they can take *la copa* {the cup} from us and keep us from dancing in the *fiesta*. They don't even believe in Santiago!"

Ambrosio, who had told his story out of one side of a mouth bulging with coca leaves, looked around to see what impression he had made. However, he did not find the sympathy he had expected. Nearly all his hearers seemed concerned about Villca.

"The *evangelistas* do believe in Santiago," Mamani said. He

21

got up from his seat. "They have a book that Santiago wrote. They practice what he taught. All these years we have not even known who Santiago was. All we knew was that plaster statue in church with the broken arm. But now Villca has explained to us all about Santiago and even read to us from the book Santiago wrote."

Mamani bade them all *hasta mañana* (good-bye), and they agreed to come the next day to start making adobe bricks.

"I am sorry I will not be here myself," Mamani said. "I must go to Azangaro the first thing in the morning and see what I can do for Villca."

Next morning when Mamani arrived in Azangaro, he heard that a new police officer had come from Puno, the capital of the department. He had taken over as new chief of police in the province. The office at the police station was neat, but simple and modest—whitewashed walls, two chairs, and a small table covered with green flannel. That was all. The complete office file hung on nails in the wall behind the officer's chair. Covering the different items on each nail were neat red glossy cardboards with the insignia of *La Guardia Civil Peruana* (The Peruvian Civil Guard).

Mamani stood in the corner of the office and waited. The officer, whom he heard addressed as Captain Ramos, talked to several other people. Finally he looked at Mamani and asked, "What can I do for you?"

"*Mi capitán* [My captain]," Mamani greeted with both hands and bowed toward the officer. "I have come to inquire respectfully about my friend, Celestino Villca, whom I understand you are holding here."

Captain Ramos did not speak Quechua fluently, but enough to understand and to make himself understood. "You mean the Adventist whom they brought here yesterday?"

"Yes, sir; he is a good man. He is not a thief."

"Oh, no. I know, the Adventists are not thieves. I have been to the meetings of the *gringos* [foreigners]. Adventists do not drink or use coca. They are honest and clean people, and we never have trouble with them." The officer drew a deep breath like a sigh.

"That is what I told Señor González's overseer. He had beaten the Adventist badly. Those stupid people think they serve their country and the church by hurting a man just because he is of a different religion."

Mamani felt relief and surprise replace the dread that had lain in his stomach ever since Ambrosio brought his bad news yesterday. He was not used to hearing police officers talk like this. He almost got the impression that the captain himself was an Adventist.

"*Tayta* [Papa]," he said, "are you an Adventist?"

"Oh, no, certainly not." Captain Ramos acted much offended. "I am an apostolic Roman Catholic!" He pounded a ruler on his table to emphasize each of the last three words. "But," he pounded again, "I wish Peru had many more who, like the Adventists, try to live honest, clean Christian lives."

"Señor Villca is not here then?" Mamani ventured to ask.

"No, I know better than to arrest honest men who are going about their legitimate business. Señor Villca is not here. He left my office at once, and I do not know where he went."

As Mamani walked out from the police station and down the street he felt happy. He was glad that Villca had not been jailed. And knowing that God had protected His servant gave Mamani real joy and satisfaction. He had trusted in God, and God had not failed him.

He looked all about as he walked the streets and the plaza, thinking he might find Villca, but he did not find him.

"He must have gone to some other town or back to Juliaca," Mamani thought.

He stopped on the sidewalk across from a two-story building with an oval shield over the broad, open doorway. Mamani could not read what it said, but he recognized the official sign of a public school. He knew that it was the boys' school and that the director was the school commissioner of the province. Before the people of his village could build a school, they would have to get permission from this commissioner. He hesitated for a moment.

"Now that I am here," he thought, "maybe I should talk to the man about our plans. Or should I wait for a later opportunity?"

He almost turned away, but then decided to go in. Carefully

23

When the director looked up from his papers, Mamani bowed. "Tayta, buenos dias," he said, holding his hat awkwardly.

he looked through the hallway into the patio behind. He could hear a teacher in one classroom talking, and in another classroom the mumbling of boys reciting in unison. As he hesitantly walked through to the patio, he passed an open door. Inside the room a man sat at a desk.

"That must be the director," Mamani thought. He turned back to the open door. With his hat in both hands he bowed several times as he entered.

The director sat behind piles of books and papers. On the walls Mamani saw maps, and behind the man he recognized a picture of General San Martín and another of Simón Bolívar, the great heroes and liberators of Peru. The man was neatly dressed in a black suit and white shirt, but he did not look like a man from the coast. He looked like a *cerrano* (mountain man) from the highlands, a man like Mamani.

Mamani waited awhile inside the door. When the director looked up from his papers, Mamani bowed. *"Tayta, buenos días* [Papa, good morning]." He held his hat awkwardly under his chin.

"Come in," the director greeted in perfect Quechua. "Come in; sit down. I am here to serve you." He smiled at his visitor and showed him a chair.

Mamani felt at ease, but he scarcely knew how to begin. He just said, "We want a school in Condorrumi."

"Splendid! There is nothing I would rather see than a school, not only in Condorrumi, but in every village. I regret, though, that our government does not have money at the present to establish any more schools."

"We will all go together and pay for the teacher ourselves."

"Good, that is wonderful. But first you must have a schoolhouse and a place for the teacher to live. Playground I suppose is no problem."

"With your permission, señor, we, the villagers of Condorrumi, have decided to build a school and a house for the teacher."

"Certainly you have my permission, but you don't need any to build a schoolhouse on your own property. Go right ahead with your plans, and when you are ready, let me know and we will try to find a teacher for you. It will not be easy, though."

25

The Schoolhouse Burned Twice

The director got up from his chair and came over to shake hands with Mamani. "I congratulate you and your neighbors and wish you success in your plans for a school. I would like to see many other villages follow your example. Someday I hope to visit Condorrumi, and we will get a license for a private school until the government can establish one."

All the way home Mamani felt like singing praises to God. He had gone to Azangaro with a heavy feeling, but now the sky seemed bluer, the grass greener, the people friendlier, and the bird songs livelier. Yes, all nature seemed to prove the words of Villca's little song: "God loves me."

Building Adobe Walls 4

Night had begun to fall when Mamani arrived home from Azangaro. The villagers had been busy all day making the first preparations for their school building. They had gone home by now, but Mamani was pleased to find that a good deal of work had already been done in preparing the ground and digging a foundation.

Juana told him that most of the conversation among the villagers while working had been about the visit of Celestino Villca and Ambrosio's story of how he had been treated at the hacienda. "They are all coming back tomorrow to hear how your visit at the police station turned out."

If the enthusiasm over the school plans had been great before, it certainly was even greater after Mamani told his experiences with Captain Ramos and the school commissioner. Now all their fears disappeared because they could work with confidence. They worked hard, and many of them came almost every day. Soon they had a good foundation laid. Adobes were scattered over the school ground to dry in the sun. The piles of these dry mud bricks grew rapidly as the people brought them from their own homes where they had stored them for other purposes. They brought other materials, and even Ambrosio brought his part. Although his own vices led him to hate the *evangelistas* and all thought of reform, he wanted his children also to have the benefit of a school.

The feast of *Todos los Santos* (Halloween) came and went with all its traditions and celebrations at home and in town. Offerings were made at midnight for the dead at the cemetery, and the women baked cake dolls to be eaten at the feast. But, in spite of diversion, work advanced rapidly on the school.

The Schoolhouse Burned Twice

After about four weeks had passed, one of Mamani's neighbors suggested, "Let us start the building now. If we wait until after the rain, we may come to the first of April, the day that schools open, without a school building."

Mamani listened thoughtfully to his neighbor's suggestion. It was noontime, and the men had been working hard since early morning. Now they each sat on an adobe around a colorful shawl on which Juana had piled many unpeeled boiled potatoes, sun-dried lamb, soup, and corn.

"That sounds like a good suggestion to me," said Mateo Quispe, Mamani's nearest neighbor and a hard worker. "We have a good solid foundation laid and almost enough adobes. I am sure we can get the walls up and maybe the roof over before the rain starts."

Others agreed, urging that construction be started as soon as possible. Mamani peeled a long purple potato. He had not said anything, but he looked around at his neighbors with satisfaction. He felt glad because they also were anxious to get the school built.

"If you all agree, we will start building as soon as enough adobes are ready," Mamani said. "Maybe the teacher will be willing to come a month or two before school so that he can help us and encourage all the parents to enroll their children."

"We will need wood for the sleepers over the door and windows," someone observed.

"Yes, I will call a meeting and have everyone fill his quota for the expenses," Mamani answered. "But still the doors and windows will have to wait. We will buy them at next year's fair."

The pile of potatoes and lamb was rapidly disappearing, and the neighborhood women helped Juana carry away the empty plates.

The man sitting next to Mamani dipped a potato in a little plate of coarse salt, then turned to him. "What about the teacher? Who will he be?"

"I will soon go to Juliaca and Puno to make the arrangements for one, and I will bring back the news."

The villagers began work on the building. The walls of the schoolhouse were to be high so there would be no doubt that it was a schoolhouse. One big door would lead out to the playground in front, and a small door would lead from the back. A window would be placed at each side of the big door.

Mamani stayed another two weeks and worked with the neighbors until the walls were high enough to reach the opening for the windows. Then he left for Juliaca. He gave last-minute instructions for the construction to Mateo Quispe, who would direct the work until Mamani returned. As soon as the walls were up, Mamani cautioned, they should be topped with plenty of straw weighted down with heavy stones, so that they would be protected should the rain come.

Mamani gazed at Juana with love as he bade her good-bye the morning he left on his trip to Puno. Little Jacinto ran along with his father all the way to the place where the small path met the road.

"Good-bye, Papa. Good-bye. Good luck. Greet Celestino in my name, if you see him."

Mamani lifted the boy up in his arm and hugged him. "Good-bye, Jacinto. Be a good boy. I will come back soon. Run along now to Mamma, and be good to her."

Jacinto walked backward a little way waving with both hands, then he stood with his eyes on his father until he saw him disappear behind the hill.

It was early, just after dawn. Mamani had a long way before him. The cold morning air did not bother him, for he walked briskly. He could hear the church bells in Azangaro calling early mass. There were few travelers on the road until he neared Santiago in the early forenoon. Then he had plenty of company, because people from surrounding villages were coming to town for the Sunday morning market. Women in bright *ñiglias* (shawls) and colored skirts carried bundles of fresh potatoes, frozen dehydrated potatoes, *ocas* (a kind of sweet potatoes), and *quinua* (small seed used for food) on their backs, and men in colored ponchos drove burros loaded with sacks of produce they had to sell from their small farms. Many brought big sacks of sun-dried cow dung and llama droppings, fuels that sold easily in town.

People, buying and selling, filled the plaza. Merchants sat in

29

rows on the ground with their wares spread before them. Mamani knew many of the merchants—the potter with his bowls and pots of all sizes and shapes; the druggist with dozens of small woven sacks of strange dried fruits, seeds, and herbs; and the butcher with dried and fresh meat.

Mamani had no time for Sunday shopping. He had to hurry on. But before he continued his journey, he went, as was his custom, into the church for a moment of worship. Mamani paused before the image of Santiago. The saint had the same straightforward look. "Thou shalt not make any graven image . . . : thou shalt not bow down to them," he remembered, and so bowed his head only slightly.

Somehow Mamani felt different from usual in church. Before, he had always come with a selfish desire for Santiago to help and protect him. Now he felt a desire to please God. He felt a need of God's forgiveness, and from his heart a prayer for God's mercy and help went up to the throne of grace. He had not sprinkled holy water or made the sign of the cross, nor had he bowed down to any saint. Yet he felt a greater peace and joy than he had ever felt before. But as he left, he could not help turning to bow his head in the direction of the altar.

About noon he reached the Cuzco railroad, and all afternoon he followed the tracks until he arrived at Juliaca. What a long walk it had been. Mamani felt very tired and let himself drop down to a bench on the plaza by the railway station. He was glad he had finally arrived, because he felt he could walk no more. Lucky, he thought, that it had been a cool, cloudy day. How clean and orderly Juliaca was. He looked with admiration at the streets and houses. He would like to see more of the town, but right now he only hoped he could find a place to sleep.

A young Indian had come to sit on the same bench.

"Do you know Celestino Villca?" Mamani asked him.

"No." The young fellow looked surprised.

"Do you know the Adventists?"

"I know the Adventist clinic," said the young man, seeming to pick up interest. "I have my sick mother there."

"Adventist clinic? The Adventists have a clinic here in Juliaca?"

30

"Oh, yes, a good one—'Clinica Americana.' It is right over this way, just two blocks from here." His voice was friendly. "I will show you, if you like. Maybe they will know about your friend Villca."

"Thank you. It surely is nice of you." They walked together across the plaza and along the narrow sidewalk of a street.

"Here it is, right here," the stranger said, pointing toward a newly constructed low building with big windows. They entered through a wide doorway and came into a patio with grass and flowers. The nice building surrounded the patio on all sides. Through an opening at the left corner came a man dressed in white with some shiny metal tubes hanging from his neck.

"That is the doctor," said Mamani's new friend.

"*Ola* {Hello}, Isidro," the doctor greeted, and then he smiled at Mamani. "*Buenos dias, amigo* {Good morning, friend}. I have not met you before. Can I do something for you?"

"Thank you, doctor. Mamani is my name. I come from Azangaro and am on my way to Puno in search of a teacher for my village." Isidro translated for him. "I have a friend called Celestino Villca, who is an Adventist. Would you know him?"

"No, I am sorry. I have not been here very long. In Puno they will know; but you can't go to Puno tonight. You had better stay here with us till tomorrow."

"Thank you so much, doctor. It is very kind of you."

"There is no bed available, but we have a good room in the rear with a wooden floor where you can sleep. Isidro will show you."

"What a good man the doctor is," said Mamani as Isidro led him to his lodging place.

"Yes, he is. And he really believes in God. He never does an operation without first praying for divine help."

Mamani was soon resting in a corner on some heavy blankets a young boy had brought him. It was too early to sleep. He just felt very tired. After a short while he heard music and singing, the same kind of singing Villca had taught him in Condorrumi.

"It is Villca who is singing," Mamani thought.

He could not resist. He had to go and find out. Guided by the sound, he soon found his way to the door, where he stood listening and peeping through the door crack.

"Come right in," a girl with a white cap on her head said. She had come up behind him and now opened the door and went in, holding it open for Mamani. She smiled kindly, and Mamani followed her to a chair she showed him.

It was nice and warm inside. Mamani could see that it was the kitchen and dining room of the clinic. A lady was playing a small portable organ. He had heard organ playing before in church, but this was the most beautiful music he had ever heard. At the end of a table stood the doctor. He nodded at Mamani and sang with enthusiasm. However, Villca was nowhere to be found.

Mamani could not understand anything the doctor said during his brief talk, nor what the doctor read from the Bible. But Isidro prayed in Quechua, and the singing sounded wonderful. How he enjoyed it!

During the evening, before Mamani fell asleep, he heard more singing from one of the rooms. How wonderful, he thought, to be among such people. How wonderful that he had found this good place. It must be God who had led him. The thought was sweet, and he felt very thankful.

To Puno for a Teacher 5

Puno, capital of the southeastern section of Peru, looked strange to Mamani. He had never before been in this important port on Lake Titicaca, the highest navigable lake in the world. The altitude, 12,600 feet above sea level, did not bother him or interest him at all. He found it normal. But the enormousness of the body of water greatly impressed him.

From the heights overlooking the city, Mamani had a gorgeous view of the secret Titicaca of the Incas. The lake sparkled in the beautiful morning sunlight, its waters extending as far as Mamani could see. On the distant skyline the mountains of Bolivia lifted their snowcapped peaks into the deep blue heavens. Below him lay the city, peaceful in the bright, thin air. He saw the tall steeples of churches and hundreds of red-tiled rooftops among towering eucalyptus trees, with a sprinkling of shiny tin roofs between.

The night before Mamani had found lodging in the home of an Aymara Indian. The house was in a little village on a hill overlooking the city. From that high point the city spread its marvelous pattern of lights before him. He had never seen such a sight. After his long, tiresome day visiting in Juliaca and walking the thirty miles to Puno, Mamani felt tired. He felt glad to have reached his destination. Next morning, refreshed by a good night's rest, he walked down the winding road which widened to a narrow street.

The people did not speak Quechua, so it was not easy for Mamani. They spoke Aymara, the other of the two highland Indian languages. He felt almost as though he had entered a strange country.

He came to the harbor and stood marveling at the sight of a

large steamer being loaded by a crane. Not far from him stood an Indian like himself, who also watched with interest.

"Maybe this Indian can help," he thought.

"Please tell me," Mamani said, "do you know where the Adventist evangelist lives?"

The Indian understood and answered in halting Quechua. "The *gringos Adventistas* [foreign Adventists] live in Platería."

"Platería, where is that?"

"In Juli, just on the other side of Accora."

"But don't the *gringos evangelistas* have a house here in Puno?"

"Yes, I guess so. I have seen them in Lima Street. I think they live in Señor Aragon's house. They have meetings there."

"Have you been to their meetings?"

"No, not here. I have been many times to the meetings in Platería. I live there. They have meetings *los sabados* [on Saturdays], good meetings. Many come from villages all around."

Mamani wondered. "Do they always have meetings on Saturday?"

"Yes, the Adventists always have meetings on *sabado,* also here in Puno and in Juliaca."

"Do you have a school in Platería?"

"Oh, yes. We have had school for several years now, and many of our young people know how to read and write. It has been a wonderful thing for us."

Now Mamani really was interested. He asked many questions, and they had a long conversation about schools and teachers, and about Adventists too. When he finally left the Indian, he felt encouraged.

He followed the railway tracks from the harbor back to the station, as the man from Platería had indicated, and turned left two blocks up the street.

"It must be here," he thought, "on one of these corners."

He looked at all four of them. Stores stood on two, and one was just surrounded by walls. "This must be the one." He crossed over and asked the man who stood in the door of one of the stores.

"Is that the house of Señor Aragon?" He pointed across the street.

34

"Yes, it is. He is not there, though. He is in Lima."

"Do the Adventists live there?"

"Yes, that is the place. Go on in. You will find them."

Mamani soon stood in a very neat little patio elaborately paved with small white and black stones which formed beautiful patterns. The walls were whitewashed and the woodwork neatly painted. On two sides large tin cans held growing flowers. What a nice place. Through an open window he could hear a woman singing softly while she worked, and a child chattered. The woman stepped outside, shaking a piece of cloth. When her eyes caught Mamani, she came toward him smiling and extended her hand.

"*Imaynalla, tayta* [How are you, Papa]?" she said very kindly. Mamani felt surprised that a *gringa* should greet him in the Indian language, and when he politely shook her hand, he had a feeling of meeting a genuine friend.

A little light-haired *gringa* girl came running out. She also came and shook hands with Mamani. "*Buenos dias; como está usted* [Good morning; how are you]?" Her smile touched his heart. He had never seen a white man's child greet an Indian in such a kind way.

The conversation between *la señora gringa* (the foreign lady) and Mamani, with her speaking broken Spanish and him speaking Quechua, did not bring results.

Then the *gringa* called over her shoulder in a strange language. A neat-looking Indian girl came through the door. She smiled broadly while the *gringa* spoke more to her in the strange language. Mamani thought he had never seen an Indian girl so clean. Now the girl turned to Mamani and spoke:

"The missionary husband will not be back until tomorrow."

"*Gracias* [Thanks]," he said as he bowed and retreated slowly backward. "I will be back then," he added in Quechua.

Although Mamani felt a little disappointed because he did not find the missionary home, he felt satisfaction over his brief visit with the family. And now that he had to wait a whole day he decided to visit Platería, the village where the Indian he had met lived. Mamani wanted to see the school.

He got to the school soon after midday, and teacher and students appeared to be busy with important studies. The missionary family had gone out visiting, but the schoolteacher took an interest in Mamani when he heard about the plans for an Adventist school near Azangaro. He invited him to visit the classes, and he even brought the whole school out to march for him with its band of horns and drums. Mamani could not have been more favorably impressed. How glad he felt that he had the opportunity to see a real Adventist school in session, and he determined as never before to have a Christian school in his village before the next year.

Mamani stayed overnight in Platería. The teacher invited him to his house to sleep and to have supper and breakfast. Mamani enjoyed talking to him about the school and its activities.

From a terrace on the hill where the teacher's house stood, they could look over the plain with Lake Titicaca in the background. Hundreds of small Indian homes dotted the *pampa* (plain).

"Many of my students come from these homes." The teacher gestured with his hand to indicate the Indians' houses.

Just below them at the foot of the hill stood a large building with a high, square tower over the entrance. Mamani could see that it had been built recently. The roof of new corrugated iron glittered in the evening sun.

"What building is that?" he asked.

"That is our new Platería Adventist church. Do you want to see it? I will show it to you."

"It certainly looks nice. It must have cost a lot of money to build a church like that." Mamani admired the big whitewashed building as they slowly walked down the hill.

"Yes," said the teacher, "just think of it. Adventist believers from all over the world have sent us the money to build it."

"Are there really Adventists in all parts of the world?" Mamani looked at the teacher with surprise.

"Yes, and they all give an offering every Sabbath, and from that offering they helped us to build our church."

"Why do the Adventists worship God on Saturday?" Mamani had wondered about this question since he had talked with the Indian at the harbor.

"The Bible teaches us to do so. The Ten Commandments say

that we should keep holy the Sabbath, the seventh day." The teacher knew the fourth commandment by heart, and repeated it.

"So the commandment actually says that 'the seventh day is the Sabbath of the Lord thy God,'" Mamani said with wonder.

"Strange," Mamani thought, "that most Christian people keep Sunday when the commandment says so clearly to keep the seventh day, which is Saturday."

Next day Mamani presented himself again in the patio at Lima Street. This time the missionary, a tall *gringo,* met him and spoke kindly. A bright-looking young Indian translated for them.

"I am so sorry to tell you that we will not be able to provide you with a teacher this year." The missionary looked sad and serious. "We certainly would like to help you, but we simply do not have teachers to meet the many calls that are coming from all sides."

Mamani sat speechless. He had not expected this disappointment. Could it be possible? No teacher? No teacher? He felt stunned.

"I know that you and your neighbors will feel bad." The missionary seemed to sense his visitor's feelings. "In many places the people are disappointed over not being able to have a teacher. But don't get discouraged. Go right on with your plans. Trust in God. He will provide when it is His time."

"But I came so early. There are still three months till school starts," Mamani begged.

"I know; but I also know that we have more schools than teachers. We will not have enough Aymara-speaking teachers, and in Quechua it will just be impossible."

Mamani felt like crying. How could he go back to Condorrumi and tell his neighbors that they could not have a teacher?

The missionary read a few encouraging verses from the Bible and then asked Mamani to kneel with him while he prayed to God for a school and a teacher in Condorrumi. He also prayed for Mamani, his family, and his neighbors.

When they stood up after the prayer, Mamani felt sure that God would help, and he knew that the missionary was just as much interested as he in a school for Condorrumi. He also sensed that

37

the *gringo* had great love and a deep interest in him and his neighbors.

"I will tell you one thing which you might do," said the missionary as he accompanied Mamani through the patio to the street exit. "We have just sent a young missionary with his family to Llallahua. Maybe he can help you. He is going to build a mission station and open up schools among the Quechuas." The missionary gave Mamani an encouraging smile and shook his hand vigorously. "You go there and see him on your way back to Azangaro."

"I certainly will." Mamani felt more encouraged by this news.

"We have a meeting tonight. Won't you come and join us?" The missionary still held Mamani's hand and shook it once more.

That night Mamani attended the meeting, and although he understood only part of what was said, he felt even more encouraged.

The road back seemed longer to Mamani. Much of the time he thought about the message he had to bring back: No teacher!

It was almost sundown Friday when he came to the *pampa* of Llallahua, where he had heard that the *gringo misionero* and his family had come to live.

"Where are you going?" A man and his wife overtook him on the path.

"In the direction of Santiago. Where are you going?"

"To the meeting of the *gringo misionero*."

Mamani stood still. "To the *Adventistas*?"

"Yes, come along. We are building a school there. Tonight at sundown the missionary will speak to us at a meeting."

Mamani could think of nothing he would rather do. He soon found himself among a small group of Quechuas gathered inside the walls of a spacious new adobe building. The four adobe walls stood without a roof to cover them, and the setting sun shone through open window holes.

Not many came to the evening meeting, but church service the next day overflowed with people who came from every direction over the *pampa*.

The missionary was a tall, strong *gringo*. A young Indian translated his sermon into Quechua. Other Indians offered prayers and led the singing in Quechua. As the missionary spoke of the love of God for everybody—poor Indians as well as rich landowners—Mamani felt happiness swell within him. He longed more than ever to become a real child of God.

That afternoon as Mamani started on the road home, he noticed the missionary talking with Indians in the yard behind the school building. Mamani turned back. Here was his opportunity to ask for a teacher.

"Don't worry," the missionary assured him. "As soon as I can, I shall visit Condorrumi; and we will somehow find a teacher for you."

As Mamani traveled across the pampas toward Condorrumi, he remembered the missionary's words. "We will somehow find a teacher for you." Mamani believed him to be a man of God. Surely God would provide the teacher that Condorrumi needed so much.

39

"What do these Indians want a school for anyway? They are better off without it." The men were drinking and arguing.

Straw Roof in Flames   6

Darkness had fallen when Mamani reached Santiago, so he decided to spend the night there. In the town he met two of his neighbors. They told him that Señor González had come by Condorrumi and had been furious to discover the villagers building a schoolhouse. This news worried Mamani, but he decided not to talk about the school until the next day when they could all meet together.

Morning dawned cloudy and windy. As ever when the sun did not shine, it was bitterly cold. Mamani still lingered in Santiago when a hailstorm suddenly broke loose, and everybody in the busy Sunday morning street rushed for shelter. He hurried to the nearest house, where a white rag on a stick over the door told him that the host welcomed customers for a drink of *chicha*. People crowded into the *chicha* parlor. At the table every place had been taken by some low-class townspeople and farm overseers. He found a place on a gasoline box and sat there with his back to the table.

Some of the men argued in loud voices. Mamani heard Llallahua and the *gringo* mentioned. He started to fish for something in his bag so that nobody would notice him listening. The hostess kept very busy with customers at the table. She did not ask Mamani for his order, and he decided not to order any *chicha*. He thought of Villca who said, "No *chicha!*"

"They will never permit that," one fellow at the table was saying, and he banged his big glass hard on the table for emphasis. "They will kill the *gringo* first."

"And what do these Indians want a school for anyway? They are much better off without it. They don't need to read. They are happy and have plenty to do. Why do they want to bother with a school?"

"The *gringo* wants to teach them to read the Bible," one said, and a corner of his mouth turned up in a sarcastic grin. They all laughed.

"*El Padre* Medrano will never like that."

"Of course not—not a school of the missionaries. He is afraid all his Indians will become *evangelistas*."

"That would ruin our business with alcohol and coca."

"That is what I say," volunteered a big man with a red face and black moustache. "It is in the best interest of us all that these brute Indians be kept ignorant."

Then he smiled and spread his arms wide. "But friends, what are we worrying about? The landlord will see to it that these rebellious Indian leaders are either killed or thrown in jail. He will teach all the Indians in Llallahua a good lesson. You wait and see."

Mamani had heard enough. He flipped the strap of his bag onto his shoulder and walked to the door, where he stood until the shower stopped.

The news of Mamani's return spread through his community, and early next morning the villagers gathered in their leader's patio. Even Ambrosio sat among the crowd, though he had to shirk his farm labor to come. Mamani figured Señor González would no doubt forgive Ambrosio so long as he did his duty well as a spy.

Mamani spoke in detail about his visit to *Clinica Americana*, Platería, and Puno. The villagers listened with interest. Although the prospect of getting a teacher soon sounded discouraging, the enthusiasm for a school did not seem to lessen. The news about an Adventist mission being established in Llallahua especially filled the villagers with satisfaction. Somehow they trusted the *gringo* would be able to help them in their own struggle. Mamani did not mention the conversation he had overheard at the *chicha* parlor in Santiago.

Ambrosio, who had begun chewing his coca harder than ever, seemed anxious to say something. Mamani gave him a sign to go ahead.

Ambrosio rose and spat. "I just want to warn you," he said. "*El patrón* González will not permit it. It is of no use to plan for a school."

The villagers usually did not talk against the landlord, but today they seemed bolder. They talked almost all at once.

"Señor González does not own us. We are not his slaves."

"We are building our own schoolhouse on our own property."

"There is liberty in Peru. Our government is in favor of education for all."

"The school commissioner is in favor."

Ambrosio shook his head. "Yes, I know. But you know González. I warn you."

Mamani feared that Ambrosio was right. But he would not for anything discourage his neighbors.

"Tell Señor González, if he asks, that we have suspended the building for the present." Mamani nodded to Ambrosio. "And in the meantime," he looked around at each one, "let us all show our faith in our school project by contributing straw and poles for the roof so that all will be ready for the great day when we will thatch our schoolhouse."

Almost three weeks passed. Condorrumi lay peacefully in its mountain nook. The villagers who sensed possible trouble ahead for their school seemed even more determined. The stock of straw, poles, and canes piled up inside the finished walls of the school. They were almost ready to begin the roof.

Mamani sat in his patio making straw ropes. They would need a lot of them for the roof. Between his toes he held the finished rope, shifting it as he progressed with the work. He worked fast, and Jacinto helped him, handing him the selected wet straw in neat small bundles. It was early afternoon.

"Look! Who is coming?" called Juana, running into the patio. "We are going to have visitors." She had been first to see four horses approaching in a cloud of dust.

Mamani got up, and his eyes lighted with excitement. "It is the *gringo,* the pastor *evangelista* from Llallahua!" They rushed to receive the visitors.

The Schoolhouse Burned Twice

The missionary shouted a greeting, jumped from his horse, and helped his wife down from hers.

"*Como está* Mamani? Here we are, the whole family. You know my wife; and look, here I made saddle boxes for the children so that they could come along too." Two strong wooden boxes hung one on each side of the third horse, and each held a child, one three and the other about four years of age.

The interpreter who accompanied them got off his horse and came forward repeating the *gringo's* words in Quechua.

The visitors rested awhile; then the missionary suggested that they go visiting. First Mamani took them to the adobe schoolhouse. Then he took them to visit neighbors.

Mamani accompanied them all afternoon. In every home the missionary and his wife spoke words of encouragement, and they invited everybody to come to a meeting in the evening. Most of the villagers welcomed the visitors immediately. A few were a little fearful at first, but the missionary captured their hearts with little effort. They could all understand the language of true kindness, and they all loved the two *gringo* children, who already had learned a bit of Quechua. Before sundown they met in Mamani's patio for a religious service, and they had another meeting early next morning.

"Have faith in God," the missionary told them. "If it is His will, you will have a school. Go ahead and finish your schoolhouse, and I will promise you a teacher." *El gringo* put his arm around his interpreter. "If we do not find a teacher, I will give you Antonio." He patted Antonio on the shoulder.

After the missionary's visit, nothing could stop the villagers of Condorrumi. They wanted the school roofed and ready when the promised teacher came. And so a few days later, Mamani called his neighbors together for the big event, the thatching of their schoolhouse.

The rainy season had begun. There had been many gray and rainy days, but now the sky cleared. The happy, enthusiastic villagers in Condorrumi gathered by their schoolhouse. The men brought tools and bundles of long, thin leather strips soaked in water for binding the roof poles together. The women brought pots of soup as well as potatoes and other vegetables for the meals.

Mateo Quispe directed the work, and they all worked hard. Mamani felt a happy satisfaction, but once in a while the thought of Señor González and what he had heard in the *chicha* parlor in Santiago came over him like a dark cloud. Ambrosio did not come.

Part of the rafters were up and the framework of the roof was taking shape when a dust cloud in the road revealed an approaching horseman.

"Señor González is coming," shouted one of the men on the roof.

One woman screamed, "Ay—ay, ay!" But the men continued their work with grim, determined expressions.

The landowner pulled his big horse to an earth-scratching stop. "What is going on here? What are you Indians doing?" He turned to Mamani, who kept his eyes on his hands as he approached the *patrón*.

"How do you do, Señor González. We are building a house."

"You are building a school. I know! And with what right? Who gave you permission?"

"My neighbors are helping me to build a house on my own property. I need no permission for that." Now Mamani looked straight at *el patrón* with a boldness he had never felt before. "And besides, the school commissioner in Azangaro, Señor Cabrera, gave us permission to build a school."

González raised his arm as if he would hit Mamani with his whip. "I told you that I would not tolerate that!" He cursed Mamani. "You stop this nonsense at once or I will see to it that you do." Then he jerked his horse around and galloped off in a cloud of dust toward Azangaro.

A gloomy dismay settled over the villagers, who had been so enthusiastic before. No one said much. A few of the women even cried.

"Whether he wants it or not," said Mateo, "we must get the roof finished. More rain will come, and we cannot leave it half done." And so they worked on with even greater urgency.

As the hours went by and the work progressed, they began to feel better again, and a good meal helped build new courage.

The man pushed Mamani and threw the fire onto the roof.
The evening wind fanned it to flame. The roof was burning!

When the sun turned orange and the shadows grew long, when the yellow straw on the almost-finished roof turned gold in the setting sun, the whole community rejoiced. Their school looked beautiful.

The men were putting the last touches on the roof when one scrambled down with a cry.

"They are coming. They are coming from Azangaro!" A group of horsemen could be seen coming up the road.

The Indians knew what this meant. They had built-in knowledge from generations of oppression. The women hid themselves hurriedly in the houses, and the men gathered in small groups in front of their new school. In a matter of minutes the *caballeros* descended on the villagers like a whirlwind. There was no talk or explanation—just abusive words, swearing, and oaths. Mamani could see that the horsemen had been drinking heavily.

Without stopping, they came with lifted whips and clubs at the groups of Indians. The Indians fled in fear. Some of them were trampled to the ground by horses and others suffered blows from the men. They all ran as fast as they could to their homes, chased like animals by their cruel tormentors. Mamani did not know many of the horsemen, but he recognized the *comisario* (deputy) of the subprefect, the *sacristan* (sexton), two policemen, and Señor González, who sat on his horse delivering a flood of curses. Mamani fled to the corner of his house. From there he watched the drunken horsemen. He saw González draw his horse close to one of his overseers and say something to him.

The overseer jumped from his horse and went to one of the small fireplaces where the women had cooked soup. He caught up a burning piece of wood and waved it in the air to revive the flame.

Mamani's heart hammered in his chest. "No, no!" he cried in desperation, and ran toward him. "No, no!" But the man pushed Mamani away and threw the fiery wood onto the newly thatched roof. Then he turned and aimed a terrible blow at Mamani's face. Laughing, he mounted his horse again. Mamani stumbled back to his house, his face bleeding.

The spot where the burning stick had landed smoked for a few minutes, but the lively evening wind soon fanned it to flame. The new roof was burning!

González called his men, and they went away still cursing and laughing, as the villagers watched from their hiding places to see their costly roof light the darkening sky.

The cries of villagers filled that smoke-filled evening. After all their work, no roof! The men gathered in the light of the smoldering fire. Somehow they felt consolation in being close together.

Next morning two police troopers came from Azangaro and took Mamani prisoner.

Mamani in Prison

Mamani stopped walking at the place where the road curved around the hill. His captors shoved him, but he paid no attention. Instead, he turned to have a last look at Condorrumi and his beloved home. Now the troopers also stopped and sat for a moment in silence.

Bathed by the golden rays of the early morning sun, the community of small Indian homes lay seemingly well-protected by the strong, rocky hill. Mamani's eyes swept over the fields, the meadow, and the pastures, to his own house and the corral with his sheep and a few llamas. And there on the wall in front of the patio stood little Jacinto waving. Juana also came and waved, but only a moment. She seemed to be in a hurry.

It was mild weather. The hills had begun to turn green from the recent rains. Condorrumi had never looked so dear and cozy to him. How he loved his home, his family, and his neighbors! It seemed he had never loved the earth as now, the good earth which gave him his daily bread, and the hills with pasture for his sheep. And the sky—he looked up at the white clouds—yes, he also loved the God who had given him all.

"*Vamos! Vamos* [Let's go]!" The stern voice of one of the troopers interrupted Mamani's thoughts. Reluctantly he tore his eyes from the scene and continued trotting along between the policemen's horses.

Jacinto had been sound asleep when the troopers came, but their rude demands for Mamani had awakened him. Mamani knew that Juana had been frightened and her heart close to the breaking point, but she had acted brave, shedding no tears.

"Don't worry about me," she told him. "As soon as I get things taken care of here at home, I am coming with you."

Mamani could not understand why he had been arrested. What accusations had been brought against him? What motives could send him to jail by armed guards? Not even the police troopers seemed to know for sure, but they had a written order from the subprefect of the province to take him prisoner to Puno. All they knew was the accusation that he led a rebellious group of Indians who had shown grave disrespect for authority.

Mamani had to trot quickly to keep up with the riding police, but he felt grateful that they allowed him to walk free. He had seen other prisoners forced to run with bound hands and pulled by a rope tied to a policeman's horse.

They had not gone more than two or three miles when a man on horseback came galloping up behind them. Mamani recognized him—Mateo Quispe, his neighbor.

The troopers reined in their horses as Mateo overtook them. He greeted them politely, and as he got off his horse he said in an encouraging tone:

"Here, neighbor, take my horse. It will be so much nicer for you and also for the gentlemen when you can ride together with them." He gave the troopers a broad smile and they nodded appreciatively.

"I will follow you together with your wife and will be in Puno to take my horse back. *Vaya con Dios* [Go with God]. I will see you"

"*Dios te pagara* [God will pay you]," said Mamani. It was all he could say, but he knew that Mateo understood how thankful he felt.

"You have good neighbors." The troopers now rode on either side of Mamani. "Is he also an *evangelista?*"

"Neither of us is yet, but we hope soon to be *evangelistas Adventistas.*" Mamani glanced back at Mateo, who walked in the direction of Condorrumi.

Juana arranged for neighbors to take care of the animals, packed some food, and then with Jacinto set out as fast as she could toward

Juliaca. Mateo and another neighbor accompanied her. Jacinto rode the burro, and Juana sometimes rode on it too. By continuing all night they were able to get to the police station in Juliaca before the troopers started out on their second day's journey with Mamani. Only for short times at resting places had Mamani an opportunity to talk with his family and hold his son in his arms, but he felt consolation in knowing they were close. However, when they reached the jail in Puno, the troopers rushed Mamani through the gate so quickly he had no chance to say good-bye to his family and friends.

The troopers, who had been quite considerate on the way, now became abusive and rough, apparently wanting to make an impression. They searched all over Mamani's body to see if he had any concealed knife or weapon of any kind, they looked through his saddlebags and blankets, and then they finally turned him over to the jailer.

"Now you will not cause any trouble for a good long time," one of the troopers said, as if his captive were a dangerous criminal. And to the jailer he said, "Be sure to keep this one well locked up."

"This way. You will be in cell number six." The jailer, a fat, sloppy man with coca in his mouth, showed Mamani to a block of cells and opened a small but strong wooden door. He pushed Mamani in, slammed the door, and locked it with a padlock as big as a hand. Then his face showed outside the small barred window in the door.

"There you are," he said with an amused expression. "I will be around to give you instructions and see what you need. Remember, nobody can talk to you until you have had a hearing, which will be tomorrow."

As the jailer disappeared down the corridor, Mamani could hear Juana and Mateo calling to the jailer, begging for permission to come in.

"Come again on Sunday. That is the day for visitors."

"Who is going to bring him his meals?" Juana's voice sounded anxious.

"You can bring him his meals three times a day if you wish, at noon and at six in the morning and evening."

51

The Schoolhouse Burned Twice

Mamani heard them plead again and argue with the jailer. Then their voices vanished in the noises of the street.

The unfamiliar noises and voices outside his cell meant nothing to him as he suddenly realized his hopeless condition. He felt sad and despondent. He knew how difficult it could sometimes be to gain freedom from a jail like this. "No, I will not give in to this gloomy feeling," he thought.

Then he spread his blankets and his poncho on a low adobe slab in one corner, the only furnishing in the little cell. He sat down and looked around. His eyes had by now grown used to the semidarkness. He did not feel guilty in any way. He had no crime on his conscience; yet these four walls, this low solid ceiling, and this dirty-smelling floor all seemed to condemn him.

"How can it be," he thought, "that God would permit me to be punished this way? Have I not trusted in God? Have I not given myself to serve the Lord? And now, why should I be here?"

He thought of Condorrumi, his neighbors, and their school. He had hoped so much for a brighter future for them. Even now a prayer went up from his heart for his fellow villagers, and somehow he felt that God would hear him. He thought of Juana and Jacinto. He knew they were not far away, and it had not been long since he had seen them. Still he had never longed so much for them as now.

He had placed the saddlebags which Juana had brought him beside the bed. He looked through them with interest. Juana had been in a great hurry when she packed the bags, but still she had managed to fix him a good lunch. They contained several small round biscuits she had baked a few days before. He pulled out hard-boiled eggs and a little boiled lamb meat. Best of all, he found plenty of toasted corn and fried *habas* (a kind of beans), both of which would keep. Then he found also his new poncho and neck shawl and a pair of sandals, the ones he had bought at the fair in Santiago. And his coca bag was fat with coca leaves, and among the leaves at the bottom he could feel money—yes, many coins. Lucky the troopers had not discovered that. But, what could this be? Still more? He pulled up a bundle wrapped in a small towel. His Bible! "How wonderful," he thought. He knew he could not read it, yet

52

he felt that somehow it would be a blessing to him. He pressed it to his heart and thanked God. "My good Juana has thought of everything," he told himself.

With the Bible, Juana had also included the songbook and the small ABC book he had bought from Villca. He knew the letters and had learned to spell a few simple words. He went over the first pages of the ABC book again and remembered what Villca had taught him. Now it held new interest for him, and he thought, "If I can do nothing else, I will try to teach myself to read. Again he looked up and thanked God. Through the little barred window he caught a tiny glimpse of a rosy sky.

Something banged against the outside of his door. He saw the jailer and heard him fumble with the big padlock. The door swung open and the man handed Mamani a clay pot hung in a white piece of cotton cloth.

"Here is your supper," he said and left, slamming the door behind him.

The law entitled Mamani to a hearing within twenty-four hours, but several days passed, and Mamani saw no judge. Apparently the judge had other cases of more importance; and so Mamani, just a rebellious Indian, could wait.

Every day the prisoners were allowed certain time in the patio, and at these times Mamani saw his fellow inmates. He enjoyed walking in the sun and breathing fresh air, but he thought it best not to have much to do with the others, at least in the beginning.

He had not been in the patio very long the first day when a tall, rather light-complexioned Indian in a worn-out soldier's uniform came over to Mamani with both hands deep in his pockets.

"What have you done?" the stranger asked.

"I am not supposed to talk to anyone," Mamani said. He looked the man over but did not feel much inclined to talk with him.

"No, you should have a hearing first, ha! Don't worry, they never give anyone a chance."

"Who are you? Shouldn't you first introduce yourself?"

"All right. I am Julio Apaza from Huancane. They had me jailed because I tried to civilize those ignorant neighbors of mine."

53

The Schoolhouse Burned Twice

Mamani knew the type. Apparently he was one of those young Indians who go to the cities and learn Spanish and also a lot of other things, mostly bad. He had probably been taken into the army, and he had come back proud, arrogant, and immoral. Mamani knew that this type would usually then return to their villages and try to set themselves up as dictators among their people.

"I am not here because of any crime," Mamani said.

"Oh, no. You are of course innocent as most of us in here," Apaza said with a humorless laugh.

"I merely tried to help my people to get a Christian school."

"Ah, an *evangelista*, ha! I like the *evangelistas*. Good people. Do you have any money? You will never get out unless you pay the judge and his *escribanos* {clerks}. Or do you have some powerful friend outside who can help you?"

Mamani paused. "Yes, I have a Friend. I trust in God. He will help me."

Visitors were allowed at the jail on Sundays. How happy Mamani felt as he went to the patio to meet Juana and Jacinto! Seeing them was enough to make him forget his troubles. Jacinto looked frightened and kept close to his mother. He stared wide-eyed at the prison inmates, many of whom looked dirty and mean.

"You are not afraid, are you, Papa, among all these bad people?"

"No, Jacinto. I am not afraid. They are not all bad, and you know God is with me." Mamani and his wife sat on an adobe bench, worn smooth from years of supporting prisoners and visitors.

"Yes, Papa." Jacinto crawled to his father's knee. "Mamma and I have asked God to protect you with His holy angels. You have not done anything wrong. You should not be in here."

Knowing that Jacinto understood made Mamani feel better. But he also wanted his son to respect the law and not grow up hating authorities and police.

"You know, Jacinto, Peru has good laws and an excellent constitution, but some authorities are not always faithful to the laws. Some judges are more interested in personal gain than in justice."

"Yes," agreed Jacinto; then he changed the subject.

"We went to Sabbath School yesterday."

"We had a wonderful Sabbath," Juana said, "and the missionary preached such a good sermon. Mateo also went with us. He had to leave for Condorrumi this morning, but he sends you greetings."

"God bless Mateo. He is a good neighbor. I am glad that he can take word back to the friends in Condorrumi about what he heard and saw in church yesterday."

"He went also with us to the young people's meeting in the afternoon," Jacinto said. "He liked it very much." Jacinto looked at his father, his face beaming with enthusiasm. Then suddenly it clouded with sadness.

"Papa," he said, "when are you coming home with us?"

The heartbreaking question from his little son caught Mamani unprepared. "Well," he said in the most encouraging voice he could manage, "tomorrow or one of the next days the judge will have a hearing of my case, and he will decide that I shall go home, or maybe stay here a short time more. God will help me."

Mamani sat up during the night and studied his ABC's by the
light of a candle. He was tempted to chew the coca leaves.

Massacre at Llallahua 8

Mamani tossed on his bed. Until nine o'clock, the hour set for complete quiet in the prison, there had been singing and even laughing from some of the cells. One man had recited poems, and from other cells had come calls of *"Bravo."* There had been shouts of *"Viva"* for various politicians, but also shouts of insult against authority or a hated landowner. The jailer had walked angrily through the halls, calling the men to order, and then everyone had quieted.

Mamani thought of his fellow inmates. The sight of these poor, ragged, barefoot men in that muddy patio kept coming back to his memory. Many of them were, of course, guilty of crimes. But there must also be those who, like himself, were innocent. They had no friends to witness in their behalf and no advocate to prove their innocence. So they stayed on, many without hope of anyone ever taking an interest in them or helping them. How fortunate, he thought, that he had found a powerful and faithful advocate in Jesus Christ.

"One!"

"Two!"

"Three!"

"Four!"

The voices of the four watchmen rang out in the silence of the night. "It is midnight now," Mamani thought. He knew that from then on the watchmen would repeat the calls every fifteen minutes all through the night. Two would call from the towers, another from the patio, and the fourth voice would echo through the corridors and cells. If one did not answer, it would be assumed he had fallen asleep, and one of the others would go and wake him up.

The Schoolhouse Burned Twice

As the night dragged on, the monotonous counting irritated Mamani. He sat up and wished for something to do. Juana had brought him a small candle. He found it and lighted it. "I will study my ABC book," he thought, and reached down in the saddlebag for it. His hand touched a little bag. Coca! A little coca would help. Since Villca's visit in Condorrumi he had not tasted a single leaf of coca. But, now, a little coca would calm him and help him go to sleep. He would just use it as a remedy. The aromatic smell of the green leaves filled his nostrils. It would be good for him.

"No, no!" he thought. "Why should I displease God again?" He closed the bag and pulled the string tight around it.

"One!"

"Two!"

"Three!"

"Four!"

Mamani tried to study his ABC's. Fifteen minutes later he heard the calls again. Now the watchman in the corridor noticed his light.

"Put out that light." The sound of the coarse voice came through the barred window in the door. Mamani snuffed out the candle and lay down again in darkness.

Next morning Mamani brought his coca bag and his ABC book with him on his walk in the patio. When he saw the Indian in the soldier's uniform, whom he had talked with the first day, he held up his fat coca bag.

"I will pay you with coca if you will teach me to read," Mamani said.

Apaza seemed delighted. "All right," he said, "give me the coca."

"Oh, no. I will give you a good treat of coca if you will give me a good reading lesson."

They sat down in a sunny corner of the patio and Mamani had his first lesson. He enjoyed it, and practicing what he had learned gave him something to do when he got back to his cell. Apaza also seemed satisfied. He promptly sold the coca to another inmate.

More than a week had passed since Mamani's arrest. He grew anxious, wondering when the judge would hear his case. Then one morning the jailer appeared outside his cell.

"Come with me. You are going to go before the judge." The jailer spoke between the bars while he stuck the key in the padlock.

Mamani put on his new holiday poncho and followed the jailer. At the entrance to the cell blocks a guard with fixed bayonet met them and accompanied Mamani through corridors to a large hall where a straight high-backed chair stood ready for him to sit on. He felt uncomfortable. In front of him stood a long table and behind it three big chairs, the one in the middle bigger than the others.

For a while he sat all alone, except for the guard at the door. Then a young man wearing a neat black suit came in. "I am Juan Antonio del Carpio. I have been asked to be your defender. Tell me all about your trouble, and I shall see if I can help you."

Mamani told the story of his and his neighbors' desire for a school and their struggle to get one.

"Good," said the young lawyer. "Just tell the judge what you have told me and answer all his questions the best you know, and I shall help you. But don't say anything about a Protestant school or a school of the Adventist mission. The judge is of the old generation. He may forgive you for anything else, but never for leaving the church and becoming an Adventist."

They could not talk longer, for now the judge, an elderly gentleman with a big graying moustache, came in and seated himself on the middle chair. An *escribano* followed and sat down on one side of the judge while Señor del Carpio, the lawyer, took the third chair.

"Are you Sergio Mamani of Condorrumi, of the district of Asillo of the province of Azangaro?" The judge looked straight at Mamani.

"Yes, sir."

"This is the first and preliminary hearing in your case. You will have an opportunity to defend yourself and to declare the circumstances and motives for your unlawful conduct. But I warn you that you tell the truth, all the truth, and only the truth."

59

The Schoolhouse Burned Twice

"Yes, sir."

Mamani had been accused not only for rebellion and disobedience to the local authorities, but for being leader and instigator of nearly every crime committed in the district, for thefts, for cattle stealing, and even murder. At a feast a drunken Indian fell over a cliff and died. Señor González had put all the blame for every crime and disorder in the district and his hacienda on Mamani.

The hearing lasted three full hours. The judge asked question after question; but Mamani, who knew his community, his neighbors, and the hacienda, could answer and explain it all in an honest and sensible way. Sometimes the judge would ask him involved questions using legal terms that Mamani had never heard before. Then the young lawyer would interrupt and ask to have the question repeated in such a way that Mamani could understand it.

When they finally came to the real issue, and Mamani told how the new school had been attacked and burned by Señor González and his men, the judge suddenly seemed to understand.

"Ah, aha," he said and paused for a long while. Then he asked, "Who gave you permission to build the schoolhouse?"

"The school commissioner of the province, Señor Cabrera in Azangaro."

"Did he give you a written permit?"

"No, sir, he said I did not need one as long as I built on my own land, and he promised that when the school building had been finished he would solicit a license from the Ministry of Education for an elementary school."

"*Bueno.*" The judge turned first to Señor del Carpio and then to his *escribano.* "We will now dismiss the hearing until we have obtained an official report of the matter from the provincial school authority in Azangaro."

He rose from his chair. "You can go now, Mamani," he said.

While Mamani had to suffer inactivity in jail, his wife Juana had difficult work to do. Caring for his food every day and at the same time for the house, the animals, and the fields, two days' trip away, drained her strength. She just could not visit her husband every Sunday no matter how much she wanted to. Weeks passed, and there appeared no sign of a further hearing of Mamani's case.

The villagers sent delegations to the subprefect in Azangaro and to the prefect in Puno with requests for his liberation, always hopeful that their petitions would soon be granted.

One Sunday morning, as soon as the gate opened for visitors, three of Mamani's neighbors hurried in. When they saw him, they exclaimed with anxiety in their voices: "Oh, Mamani, we have terrible bad news."

"Something has happened to my family?" Mamani's words trembled with fear.

"No, your family is well."

"What?"

José Condori took the lead as spokesman. Condori had been the one who first and most readily accepted the religious teachings which Villca had brought to Condorrumi.

"They have killed Mateo," he said, overwhelmed with emotion. "They have killed Mateo Quispe!"

"Mateo Quispe is dead?" Mamani's heart seemed to stop beating.

"Yes, he fell and the horses trampled him to death. I saw it, Mamani. I saw it—horrible! I shall tell you how it all happened." Condori rolled a big stone over close to the mud bench where Mamani and his friends were sitting, and sat down on it.

"The missionary in Llallahua had sent word out to all groups of Adventist believers that they were going to put the roof on the new school and church building at the mission station, and so Mateo and I went there to help with the work. We came Friday afternoon and attended all the Sabbath meetings. A great number of people were present from many places, and we had a fine Sabbath with great blessings from the Lord.

"On Sunday morning the work started on the roof. I think that nearly all families in Llallahua came to help. I never saw so great enthusiasm. We all helped willingly and with great joy. It must have been a poor Sunday in Santiago, when everybody came to Llallahua.

"I don't know if the missionary or anybody knew about it. It all happened so suddenly, late in the afternoon. Many worked up on the roof. They were first to call warning. They shouted, 'They are coming, horsemen are coming from Santiago!' A big cloud of

61

dust appeared on the road and moved quickly toward us. I never saw so many horses. There must have been people from all the haciendas and most of the *caballeros* from town. Quispe and I stood with the people on the pampa between the church and the small lake. We expected of course that those drunken riders would stop —you could see they were drunk—but they didn't. They kept right on galloping straight at us. When we realized they were not going to stop, we all scrambled for safety. Quispe did not get away. He fell, oh, he fell, and the horses went right over him—many horses, they crushed him and kicked him to death!"

Condori paused awhile. He had to control the emotion which choked his voice.

"Many others lost their lives. Those on the roof thought at first that they were safe, but when the attackers started to shoot at them with their rifles, they panicked and scrambled to get down. Some jumped, some rolled down the roof and got hurt, some died. The riders continued chasing the poor people all over the pampa and shooting at them. The missionary and his family stood in front of his house, firm and fearless. God protected them. The horsemen did not come back. But eleven or twelve persons died in the massacre! We took Quispe's body back to Condorrumi. Day before yesterday we had the funeral."

Weeks turned to months, and still Mamani hoped for another hearing. He knew the report from the school commissioner would be in his favor, but it never came. It probably had never been asked for. Some of his neighbors had gone to Señor Cabrera in Azangaro and inquired about it, but the school director said he knew nothing about a request from Puno for a report on a school in Condorrumi.

Now fewer friends came to visit Mamani on Sundays. Although he had found some new friends among the inmates, he felt more and more discouraged and lonesome. He studied hard on his reading lessons and made progress. He could already spell through a few verses of the Gospel of John. He found the greatest encouragement and relief in listening to the Word of God. A young man had volunteered to read for him from the Bible, and he explained in Quechua what Mamani did not understand. Mamani paid him a little for his trouble, and so every Sabbath he heard the words of the Bible. Soon his young reader also liked the Bible reading, and they read on other days also.

Almost six months passed, the longest months Mamani had ever known. One Sunday when Mamani sat by himself in the patio, studying his Bible, someone touched his shoulder. He turned to look.

"Villca!" Mamani jumped up and embraced his friend. "Where have you been so long, Celestino?"

"I have been away for over four months. The mission sent me to work in the provinces of Cuzco." Villca sat down on the ground, and Mamani joined him.

"Last week I went back to see the old friends and groups in the province of Azangaro, and I also got to Condorrumi. There I heard the sad story about the school and about you and Brother Quispe. I feel so sorry that all this should happen."

"How are Juana and Jacinto?" Mamani asked. "Did you see them?"

"I certainly did. They are well. Juana told me to bring you their love and to tell you that they would come next Sunday."

"Look. I was reading my Bible when you came." Mamani opened the Book and handed it to Villca. "Please read for me."

They studied and talked as long as the visitors' period lasted. Mamani had not felt so encouraged any time since he had been in prison.

"Have faith in God. Pray much," Villca said. "He will not fail you. I shall do all I can for your liberation. I shall tell the missionaries. They surely will be able to do something for you." They walked together to the gate. "Don't be discouraged. I will see you again soon."

Villca had to leave.

That week Villca talked to the young lawyer, Señor Juan Antonio del Carpio, who should have been defending Mamani.

"Not much we can do," he said. "But I shall immediately send the judge an *oficio* and call his attention to the injustice done to Mamani."

The Schoolhouse Burned Twice

The missionary traveled much, but he found time to visit Mamani on Sundays. He also talked in Mamani's behalf both to the prefect and to the judge. Each one assured the missionary in almost identical terms:

"Oh, yes, with much pleasure. I shall at once see to it that he will be released immediately. Don't worry. You can trust that I shall do all that is in my power. I am at your service."

Nothing happened, and Mamani stayed in jail. He suffered, and his family suffered. He learned a good deal of Spanish, however, and spelling and reading. He also learned patience and to pray and to trust only in God.

In spite of all efforts put forth by Villca and the missionary, six more months went by. Now Mamani had been in the jail for one full year!

Then one day the jailer opened the cell door.

"You can go now, Mamani. You are free."

Señor Cabrera 9

Mamani packed his few belongings quickly. He could not wait to get out, away from those hated walls and dusty corridors. He threw his saddlebags and blankets across his back. Mamani's first thought was to hurry from that prison before someone changed his mind. Yet he did not want to simply disappear as other paroled prisoners did. He thought of his fellow inmates, and begged the jailer to permit him to go to the patio once more.

"No, it is prohibited. You are out. You can't go to the prisoners. If you want, you can come as a visitor next Sunday." The jailer seemed as unkind as ever.

"If I could only talk to Benigno. Please do me that last favor." Mamani's voice had something in it which the jailer had to respect.

"Bueno." He locked the gate with Mamani standing outside. "I shall bring him out here."

"You are leaving!" Benigno, the young man who had so faithfully read him the Bible, looked surprised. "How glad I am to see you free. You never belonged in here. I will miss you much, and so will many others."

"Give them all my farewell greetings, and here, Benigno, I want to ask you a favor." Mamani reached down in his bag and took out his Bible. "Take this. I wish you would continue to read it for yourself and, as you have been doing, for the fellow inmates in the patio."

Benigno took the Book with obvious pleasure. "Thank you so much. I shall read it all through myself, and I promise you to read the Gospels every day in the patio for those who like to hear. You know there are several."

"God bless you, Benigno. I am sure that the word of God's Book will give encouragement to all of you. Remember the little song we used to sing together, 'My God, He Loves Me.' Have faith in Him."

"Good-bye, Mamani."

They shook hands through the steel bars.

Mamani headed straight for home. He scarcely saw the people he passed on the road. No one paid attention to him either. But if they had, they would have seen great happiness shining from his face. As he rested on the mountainside behind Puno, his eyes drank in the sight of the city and the beautiful green-bordered lake beneath the blue sky. He felt overwhelmed by God's love and mercy and goodness. Even though he had been confined in jail for a year, God had used that year to teach him faith and trust and to give him an opportunity to study the Bible and learn to read and even to write a little. He felt like singing. His voice rang out over the hills with the words, "God loves me, He saved me."

He did not stop in Juliaca but kept to the road. A strong wind blew cold in the afternoon, the bags over his shoulder and the blankets on his back weighed him down, and his legs felt sore and stiff, being unused to walking for so long. Yet he did not mind. Nothing could overshadow the wonderful joy of freedom.

Next morning, after a rest at the home of an old friend for the night, Mamani walked across the pampa toward Llallahua. At a distance he could see the mission station. "What can that be?" A flag waved the Peruvian colors, white and red, against the blue sky! At last he recognized the building beneath the flag to be the school. The roof of the school looked strong and perfect. Mamani thought of what Condori had told about the massacre. "The missionaries certainly must not have let that discourage them," he thought.

He decided not to stop at the mission station, but hearing teachers' voices coming from the school, he could not resist. He went across the playground and peered through the open door. Two teachers stood before their classes. One had two big classes in front, and one taught another at the rear. "There must be close to a hundred pupils," he thought. He saw children and young people and even adult men and women studying. "All these will soon be able to read and write," he thought. "Oh, for a school like that in Condorrumi!" He stood for a long time and observed the teachers; then he quietly went on his way.

In view of his and his neighbors' experience, Mamani had really thought it best to forget all about a school in Condorrumi; but now, when he thought of what he had just seen accomplished in spite of the trouble made by the mestizos, he could not keep from hoping that God would help His people in Condorrumi to have a school.

With mixed emotions Mamani sat down on a stone at the side of the road and looked at his village. This was almost the exact spot where he had stood a year before to have a last look at beloved Condorrumi before going to jail. Now he felt exhausted from the long walk and realized that the long months of inactivity had stolen his strength. But what a joy to see his village again! To him there could be no more lovely scenery. All along the foot of the hills he recognized the small properties of his neighbors. They were coming home now from their labor in the fields. The sinking sun made the grass roofs of the buildings glow with its golden rays. He could see his own fields, green with growing potatoes and *quinua*. And there, yes, there came Juana driving the sheep and the llamas. Jacinto rode the burro, swinging a sling by his side. Mamani's heart beat faster. "Thanks to God, I am home again." He stood up and whistled. They did not hear, but Lolo, his dog, heard. The dog had been helping to drive the flock. Now he stood for a moment with lifted ears and then came tearing over fields and stone fences straight toward Mamani, his ears now flat against his head, his tangled snarls of long hair bouncing up and down.

Jacinto and Juana looked after the dog and then saw Mamani. He could see how they hurried along the path toward him. Mamani's heart almost cried with joy over this reunion which he had longed for so often during the last year.

Back of Mamani's house stood the walls of the schoolhouse. He shuddered at the memory of that tragic day when the roof had gone up in flames. But the walls were not ruined. Mamani noticed with satisfaction how his neighbors had protected them. To prevent them from getting soaked through by the rainfall they

67

had covered them with straw weighted down with stones. "We could put a new roof on our school," he thought, but he did not want to suggest it yet. Every one of his neighbors came to see him and welcome him home that night. Nobody mentioned rebuilding the school. Mamani knew their feelings and their fears, and he understood. Why should they attempt the impossible? They were just Indians. They wanted to live in peace. Why should they risk burning or death or prison? They were busy in their fields and with their animals. "Let us forget about a school," they thought. Though they did not say these things, he could read them in their quiet faces.

Mamani also had much to do, and how he enjoyed it! He was surprised at how well Juana had done. She had worked hard, and the neighbors had helped her. The fields were sown and planted and the animals fat and well cared for. Now Mamani took over the heavier tasks of their little property, also helping his neighbors whenever they needed it. And so life continued peacefully for a while in the village of Condorrumi.

One morning several months later Sergio Mamani went to Luis Yapo's to help the neighbors lay the foundation for a house. Mamani worked with pick and shovel digging the ditches. Some others helped him, and other Indians prepared the stones with hammer and chisel. Another group carried water for mixing the mud mortar. They worked hard and, as always on such occasions, with a spirit of happy fellowship. Señora Yapo and the other women, among them Juana, began preparing dinner for the men.

Mamani leaned against his shovel a moment to rest and look out over the pampa. He saw a small figure far down the road.

"Look, over there. Someone is coming," he said. He pointed in the direction of Azangaro. The Indians watched as the figure coming toward them grew larger.

A mestizo, a *caballero*. Who could it be? Every Indian stopped working to look.

"I know," Mamani said. "It it Señor Cabrera, the school commissioner."

Señor Cabrera walked leisurely, all alone, swinging a light stick in one hand, in the other hand holding a few wild flowers he had evidently picked on the way. He wore a friendly smile as he approached the group.

"Good morning. How are you all?" he greeted them in Quechua.

"Good morning. Good morning, señor." They felt at ease with the friendly visitor. But for the difference in his clothing he could well have been one of their own.

"Today is Ascension Day and no school, you know. So I thought I would take a walk and come out and visit Condorrumi."

"Welcome, Señor Cabrera," said Yapo. "We feel honored by your presence. We hope you will stay and accept a bite of food and a plate of soup with us."

"Thank you, with much pleasure. I am glad that I found you together like this, because I want to talk to all of you."

"*Bueno*, Señor Cabrera."

"I understand you have gone through much trouble for wanting a school." He looked at Mamani. "I am sorry I could not help you."

"Yes," Mamani nodded. He did not know what else to say.

"Now I have good news for you. The Ministry of Education has given me authorization to establish a school in Condorrumi and in other places, so that the people can learn to read."

"We don't want any school, señor," interrupted one of the villagers.

"But why?" Señor Cabrera looked surprised.

"Look over there, señor," the villager pointed at the black, sooty walls of their school building.

"Oh, that can be built again. You should not let that discourage you."

"But, when a man is dead? Do you see that house over there? Mateo Quispe lived there. He is not there anymore. He died in Llallahua, helping to build a school." It was Condori who spoke now. "I saw him die under the horses. Twelve of our countrymen died that day. We prefer not to have a school, and live."

"And there is Mamani," added another. "A whole year in prison! For what! What had he done? No, señor. No school for us."

The school director looked from face to face with sympathy.

Señor Cabrera swung a light stick in one hand and carried
a few wild flowers. He had a friendly smile for the group.

"I know how you feel. You have reasons for being discouraged. But you know, my countrymen, a school is worth fighting for. Over at Llallahua they did not give up. They did not get discouraged. They have a school going right now, and many are learning to read and write."

"I guess you are right, Señor Cabrera. We should not get discouraged. I believe that someday we will have a school in Condorrumi," Luis Yapo said, but without enthusiasm. "But now let us go and have something to eat. The women have called. Everything is ready."

In Luis Yapo's patio an enormous flat stone, barely a foot high, served as a table. A long colored shawl covered it and expanded it onto the floor where additional shawls made a long table. Señor Cabrera, Mamani, Condori, and Yapo sat around the flat stone at the head of the table, and on both sides of the patio floor sat the rest of the men. While they ate, the conversation continued to center around the school.

"I will guarantee you a government license, and I may also help you find a teacher." Señor Cabrera scraped the last spoonful of soup from his clay plate. "That tasted good. Your wives are wonderful cooks."

Mamani had not taken part in the arguments for or against a school. But he realized how fortunate they were that the provincial school director was willing to join them in their fight for a school.

"We certainly appreciate your interest in us, and we respectfully accept your offer to help us get a license for our school," Mamani finally said. "However, we must not be too hasty about it. We know that Señor González will fight it with all his fury, and he will probably not have much respect for any license."

They sat long at the table and talked on into the afternoon. The visit of the school commissioner and their conversation with him impressed the villagers and influenced a change of attitude. Now they felt encouraged in their hope for a school.

But the real change of attitude and the strongest encouragement came a few weeks later, when the missionary from Llallahua visited Condorrumi. The *gringo* stayed for three days and had meetings for the villagers in Mamani's patio. Nearly all of them came,

71

and for lack of space many had to stand on the pampa outside the patio.

The missionary talked to them about the love of God, about sin and repentance, and about grace and salvation through Jesus Christ. He read from the Word of God and illustrated the truth with simple, practical life experiences so that they all could understand. And at the third meeting, all but a few surrendered their lives to the Lord and accepted Jesus as their personal Saviour.

The missionary did not talk much about a school, just enough to rekindle their interest in learning. He told them about the school in Llallahua, how much suffering it had cost the people, but also how glad they were for their school.

"You know," he explained, "a thief may steal your poncho or take your animals or your potatoes, but no one can take away what you have inside your head. What you have learned no one can take from you.

"The best you can give your children is not money or property, but a good education. You know how great an advantage the mestizos have over you because they can read and write and speak Spanish and you can't.

"God wants you to have a good Christian school where the principles of His holy law are taught and where the seeds of godly character are sown in the hearts of your children and youth. Remember, the only thing we can take with us from this earth to heaven is character. God will help you to get a school and a good teacher, if you really work for one."

School Begins at Condorrumi

Days of bright sun, lively winds, and dust, and nights of chill air marked the time of the fair in Pucara, held every year during the middle of the dry season. No other event of the year had greater significance for the people of the neighboring provinces, and especially the province of Azangaro. Indians and whites, merchants and farmers, did the bulk of their year's business at that time. From long distances people came to sell their products and merchandise and to buy what they needed. Hardware and fabrics of national and foreign makes, industrial and agricultural products, produce from the jungles and from the coast, and even oranges and bananas from Ecuador and grapes from as far as southern Chile were exchanged. No one wanted to miss *la feria de Pucara* (the Pucara fair).

In the plaza people thronged and milled around among booths, tents, eating places, and shops where keepers squatted on the ground. Booths also lined every street, and every house became a shop. On the outskirts of town, markets of livestock, pottery, wool, poles and lumber, and corrugated iron covered large areas.

Mamani walked by himself, pushing his way through the crowd of people and their burros. He had left Juana and Jacinto to look through the booths of imported fabrics and agricultural products. But he wanted to look over the livestock and building materials outside of town.

Harsh music blared over speakers in the streets, almost drowning the noisy shouting, laughing, and bargaining of the people. The hot sun made perspiration soak through his poncho, and, now and then, the wind whipped dust into his eyes.

The Schoolhouse Burned Twice

"If I had some education," thought Mamani, "if I were not just a simple Indian, I would own a horse, and could trot proudly through this crowd, and everyone would run to get out of my way."

Then immediately he felt ashamed. "No, that is not what we need a school for. It is just so that our sons can have easier lives than we, so that they can understand more of the things happening in the world."

Mamani spotted a booth selling fresh orange juice. He had not had any of that since the fair two years before, so he decided to indulge himself this once, and hoped the cold juice would help cool him off.

As he walked into the booth, he heard a voice call from behind.

"Mamani! Mamani, wait!"

He turned and saw a tall man pushing through the crowd toward him.

"Villca, my friend!" cried Mamani. "How good it is to see you. And how much I have to thank you for, all of your hard work in helping me get out of that jail." Mamani embraced his friend.

Villca laughed. "Ha! Think nothing of it. That was the least I could do for a good friend. Mamani, I am particularly glad we met today, for I have someone with me I know you will be happy to meet. Wait here and I will go get him."

Villca disappeared in the crowd, and Mamani wondered who he had with him. After a while Villca came back with a big, clean-looking young Quechua Indian.

"This is Pedro Huanca." Villca introduced his friend, and Mamani shook the young Indian's hand.

"*Camisaqui* {How are you}?" Pedro said.

"Pedro has promised me that he will go to Condorrumi and be your teacher," Villca said. "He has had two years of study at the Juliaca training school. This year he will not have enough money to continue in Juliaca, and so I asked him to help out in Condorrumi. I know you will like him."

"I am sure we will." Mamani's eyes examined young Pedro with interest. "But you know in what shape our school building is."

"It does not matter so much. I thought that he could begin with a class in some house or in your patio or even in the roofless school-

74

house. It will encourage the people so that they may be interested in getting a roof on the schoolhouse again."

Mamani felt happy about the prospect. "When can you come, Pedro?"

"Pedro and I will try to be with you for Sabbath in Condorrumi day after tomorrow," Villca said.

"Wonderful! We shall be waiting for you Friday afternoon. Please bring Bibles and songbooks."

"I shall do that, and also some books and material you will need for the school."

Mamani told the good news to a number of his neighbors whom he met that day at the fair. Then he bought a number of long poles. He did not say anything, but the neighbors noticed the poles, and they all knew what they were for. They did not talk to each other about it either, but most of them also bought some long poles.

Mamani's burro had to walk straight on the trip home. Tied on each side of it were three poles reaching four feet ahead of its ears, and in the back they lightly touched the ground.

"My poor little burro," Mamani said, "let us go." He carried one heavy pole over his shoulder himself.

A little way out of town he met one of Señor González overseers, the one who had hit Mamani and set fire to the straw roof of the school.

"What are these poles for?" he demanded.

Mamani did not answer; he acted as if he had not heard. *"Vamos,* burro {Let's go, burro}!" he shouted.

The overseer grumbled angrily something about *el patrón,* whipped his horse, and went on.

The sun broke slowly through the white morning mist. Mamani stood in his patio watching the shadows that seemed unwilling to retreat before the light. Condorrumi began to wake up. The door opened in a neighbor's house down the road. A dog barked from a distance, and Lolo answered. The hens hopped down from their places behind the houses and scurried across the yard. Roosters flapped their wings and crowed. Mamani heard Juana in the kitchen. He knew her first move would be to kneel down by the fireplace and blow new life into the sleeping embers.

Now the morning shot its golden arrows from the mountains, and the birds mingled their voices in song. It was Sabbath morning, and to Mamani it seemed that all nature joined in glorifying the Creator. This hour had always been his supreme hour for worship. His prayers consisted of praise and thanksgiving. He had heard about God's love, about grace and salvation, and about the Sabbath. He had accepted it all. But now he felt that Christ had become real, that his own conversion was real.

He remembered the meeting the night before when most of the neighbors had again gathered in this patio. He thought that Villca had been used wonderfully by God to speak to their hearts. This was to be their first real Sabbath. They had all promised that from then on they would endeavor earnestly to follow Jesus and keep His holy law. And how thankful they felt for their new teacher. They had one who would be with them, teach them to read and write, and teach them from the Word of God.

The door opened and Villca and Pedro walked out.

"Hello there, good morning," Mamani said.

"What a glorious morning," Villca answered.

"Yes," added Pedro, "we will have a wonderful Sabbath."

After morning cleanup and a good breakfast, they sat singing in the patio, and gradually the villagers joined them.

Although not accustomed to this drastic change of leaving their usual work and getting dressed and ready for meetings on Saturday, the villagers came—not all of them, but enough to fill Mamani's patio. Mamani counted thirty-eight adults present and many children. As Mamani identified the people, Pedro Huanca wrote the names of the adults in a list as members of the new Condorrumi Sabbath School. They elected Pedro as director and secretary, Sergio Mamani as subdirector, and Juana as treasurer.

Pedro Huanca taught the Sabbath School lesson. It concerned the experience of Joseph in prison in Egypt. He explained the story so well in Quechua that the people enjoyed it and understood, though few had heard it before. "He will make us a good teacher," they told one another. Villca taught them some new songs, and the day passed quickly with singing and Bible study.

Next morning Mamani and his family again went to the Pucara fair. When they came home, their little burro was once more laden with poles and also with a big load of straw. Several of the neighbors also carried roofing material. None of them said it, but they all knew it would be used for the school.

Monday morning was a great day for Condorrumi, for it was the first day of school. Children, young people, and even adults filed into Mamani's patio, all eager to learn to read. They filled every inch of the patio. A piece of black canvas nailed on the wall served as a blackboard. Although only an amateur teacher, Don Pedro did his best. His students thought he did wonderfully, because he knew how to help and encourage everyone.

As a precautionary measure they thought it best not to have school every day at the same place. The school met first at Mamani's, but all agreed to gather at Luis Yapo's house the next day and at Condori's place the third day. Each day they would meet at a different neighbor's house.

But as the school days passed without incident, the villagers decided to hold classes in the schoolhouse, even without a roof. One Sunday they plastered the walls inside, and on the following Sunday they whitewashed them. The classroom looked very neat, but it would be good only so long as the rain did not come.

The third Sabbath when they had gathered for an afternoon meeting, one of the parents spoke. *"Hermanos* {Brethren}," he said, "we must go ahead and put a new roof on our school now before the rainy season begins."

The people all looked up at their lofty ceiling which was full of clouds. They had talked about it so many times. Maybe the time had come for action.

"Good suggestion, brother," said Pedro. "I am sure it is God's will that we should have a good, safe schoolhouse."

Mamani did not reveal his happiness. Instead he cautioned, "It is a risky thing, you know; I am afraid that the mestizos at the hacienda and in town have not changed their attitude." He wanted to make sure all the villagers were really behind the idea and aware of the danger.

77

The Schoolhouse Burned Twice

"Right you are," said Ambrosio, who looked cleaner than usual. He rose to his feet. "I have my son in the school. I like our school, but I must warn you again. One day I heard the overseer tell Señor González that the people of Condorrumi were plotting again for a school. I tell you, *el patrón* did not like it at all. He cursed in ugly language and said that he would see to that."

"We will get an official written permit from the school commissioner," said one. "He has promised us that."

"What will we do if they come again as they did the last time or if they do what they did in Llallahua?"

"I know what we will do," said Pedro. "We will just flee, all of us, and hide in the mountain. I will take my students up to the cave under the rock of the condor, so when they come, they will not find anyone. God will protect us."

Ambrosio rose again. "Now is the time if we really want to do it," he said. "Señor González will travel to Lima next week. You know he is trying for a seat in the House of Representatives. He will not be home for at least three weeks."

"Thank you, Ambrosio, for that information." Mamani stood up and nodded to him. "We appreciate the help you can give us." Ambrosio sat straighter, feeling important.

"We will have to work hard during the week," Mamani said and looked around at his neighbors. "We will need to get all the necessary material. Some of us will have to go with our llamas to get more loads of straw. But let us say that next Sunday we all gather to thatch our schoolhouse. Are you in favor of that? If anyone is against it, let him speak now."

No one said a word.

Flee the Caballeros   11

Mamani's dream had come true. His village had a schoolhouse with a nice thatched roof, a teacher, and classes that met every day. Mamani could hardly believe it. Best of all, Jacinto was actually learning to read. And Mamani went to the classes himself when he had time, and his own reading improved—far better than what he had learned in prison. The students loved their teacher. And Pedro Huanca loved them in return.

Pedro called his pupils to class every morning by sounding a tin trumpet one of the villagers had given him. Pedro said he had learned to blow one in Juliaca for the twenty-eighth of July, the Peruvian national holiday. When Pedro blew his trumpet, it could be heard far around. At the sound, the children and youth would come running from every direction, a sight which never failed to delight Mamani. He went with Jacinto every morning for the worship with which Pedro began each school day. Many parents came for the worship, and they would learn with their children a new verse of Scripture every morning. As the parents left after worship, they could hear Pedro's clear voice leading his students in singing the national anthem, "*Somos libres* [We are free]." Then the classes began. When the adults had time during the day, they would drop by the school and learn from Pedro too.

It never occurred to the villagers that they had a poor school, one with no door, windows, or even a blackboard. Wind blew the dust through the holes in the walls that let in light and air. They had no furniture, just adobe benches or wooden boxes and small pieces of boards the pupils had brought for writing. And their teacher had barely four years of grammar school. But to these

79

people this was the most wonderful school in the world, for it belonged to them, and the children were learning to read, print, and write letters. What a marvel!

One day Ambrosio came hurriedly to Mamani. He chewed nervously on his coca.

"I must hurry back to my work at the hacienda," he said. "I just came to tell you that Señor González and his men are coming. He is terribly angry about our school."

"Oh, no!" Mamani cried. He could say no more. Fear seemed to push his stomach into his throat.

"This morning Señor González heard the teacher's trumpet." Ambrosio shook all over while he told his story as fast as he could. "We were in the field. He has been home only a few days."

" 'What is that' he demanded.

" 'What?' I said.

" 'That trumpet blowing.' González guessed I knew.

" 'I don't know,' I said.

" 'Don't know! It comes from Condorrumi, and you say that you don't know!'

"He looked terribly fierce, and I feared he would knock me down, so I had to tell him.

" 'The teacher!' he roared. 'You mean to tell me that you have a school in Condorrumi, and a teacher?'

" 'Yes, *tayta*,' I said.

" 'How dare they defy me! Don't they know that I am the most important and most powerful man in the province?'

"I tell you, Mamani, I never saw him so mad. Later on he sent for some of his men, and after lunch I saw them hurry off in the direction of Azangaro. Señor González took his rifle along.

"I am afraid they will be coming soon. Be careful. Now I must run." Ambrosio hurried down the path.

Mamani lifted his eyes to heaven and called upon God for help. Then he made haste to tell the teacher.

Pedro called his students to attention. "You know," he said, "we have full right to have a school. The government school commissioner has encouraged us to establish one; and he has given us a written permit. We are only following the government plan of alphabetizing. Yet there are some who are much opposed to our school. Señor González and his men may be coming today, and we don't know what they may do." The children began to murmur.

"Now, don't be afraid," Pedro said. "God will help us. We will just have school some other place. We will now take everything we have in the school and go together up to the mountain. Those of you who live close may run home and tell your parents. We will meet in the place you know under the rock of the condor."

Everyone knew the hiding place high above Condorrumi. It was not far; still it took a good while before they all reached there because of the strenuous climb. From below it appeared only as a shadow under an overhanging rock formation. But up there it proved to be a pleasant, green, fairly level plateau protected by the great rock. There, surrounded by low scrub and completely hidden away from the world below, the villagers had a splendid view over the whole community and the fields stretching over the pampa between the hills. They could see their homes, the roads, and the schoolhouse. At a distance they could see Azangaro, and even, far away, Santiago. Mamani made the climb together with Jacinto. Juana had taken the sheep and the llamas to the pastures.

"We will now continue our school," announced Don Pedro.

Pupils and the parents who had come sat down in the grass facing the teacher, who stood with his back to the mountain at the inner part of the terrace.

"Let us sing a song to begin, shall we? What shall we sing?"

"*Diosmiy munahuan* [My God loves me]!" shouted Jacinto joyfully.

And so with the beloved little song ringing over Condorrumi, a most unique school began on the rock-shaded terrace high in the Andean mountains.

Late in the afternoon one of the parents leaned over and whispered something to Pedro. The teacher continued his class but glanced often in the direction of Azangaro. After several minutes he said, "Now, class, let us not get disturbed or alarmed. *Caballeros* are coming from Azangaro. Let no one get up. But let us all stay down and keep out of sight. We can watch them, while they cannot see us."

Pupils and parents who had come sat down on the grass facing the teacher, who stood with his back to the mountain.

They saw the horsemen ride up the road and turn into the path leading to the schoolhouse. They stopped on the playground. Señor González jumped from his horse and entered the school, his gun hanging over his shoulder. A moment later he came out again, waving his arms and hands violently, apparently much disgusted. He shouted something, and some of the men went to the nearest houses.

"To our house also," Jacinto giggled. "There is no one there."

"Careful," said the teacher. "Keep sitting. They may see us."

They saw the men return from the houses, shaking their heads and shrugging their shoulders.

"They are going! They are leaving!" some of the students cheered.

"Quiet! Stay down!" the teacher commanded. "They must not discover us."

Señor González had mounted his horse and trotted down the path. He and his men went in the direction of the hacienda and the others toward Azangaro.

Up on the mountain, the people felt relieved as they watched the *caballeros* disappear in the distance. Then suddenly one of the students called out, "Look, Señor Huanca, there is smoke!"

Yes, smoke came up from the side of the straw roof which could not be seen from where they were.

"They have set fire to the roof!" Pedro's voice broke in his dismay.

Some of the parents had already begun running down the mountain, Mamani among the first.

"Be careful. They will see you," Pedro warned.

"See or no see, what about our school?" yelled Mamani. He scrambled down over the mountain, and the others followed like a herd of llamas. Their school was on fire! Before they could reach the burning building, the fire took a firm hold on the roof. They were able to save a few poles at the far end of the building, but their costly straw thatch was a total loss. Sad and discouraged, the little group of parents and students stood watching the smoldering embers while the darkness of the night once more settled over Condorrumi.

The Schoolhouse Burned Twice

"We will have school tomorrow at the same time as usual, but we will meet on the terrace of the condor," Pedro announced.

Next morning Pedro blew the trumpet with even greater energy, and his students ascended to their mountain school. Mamani wondered if the trumpet had been heard at the hacienda. Pedro would want it to be heard, he thought.

Mamani and Condori went to Azangaro to talk to the school commissioner and to report the fire to the police. They had to wait quite a while at the commissioner's office. Mamani noticed that the *comisario* of the subprefect came by twice and looked at them through the open door. But when Señor Cabrera came, he greeted them, as friendly and attentive as ever.

"They have burned our school again, *tayta señor!*"

"They have!" The school commissioner seemed indignant. "What a shame! It is a crime!" He let a book he had in his hand come down on the table with a bang. "These *caballeros* think they can defy the Peruvian government." Again he banged the table with the book.

"Unfortunately there is not much we can do about it locally. Not even Captain Ramos, the police chief, can help you, though I know he would like to. He is under the command of the subprefect, who is completely under the control of Señor González— politics, you know. However, I shall immediately send a stiff report by telegram to the Ministry of Education. Maybe González will respect orders from the minister."

A policeman appeared at the door together with the *comisario*. They did not come in, but the school director suspected their intention. He got up from his desk and approached them.

"What can I do for you?"

The policeman hesitated a little. "We came to take this man Mamani to the *subprefectura*."

"Oh, and who sent you?"

The policeman shrugged his shoulders and nodded in the direction of the *comisario*. Then the *comisario* said, "*El señor subprefecto* sent me to tell this ex-convict, Mamani, that the subprefect wants to see him at once in his office." The *comisario* talked with stubborn authority.

84

"You can go and tell the subprefect that Señor Mamani will come as soon as he can. He is occupied right now."

The policeman turned and walked off down the street. The *comisario* looked much offended. His red face got redder.

"Tell me, *señor comisario*," the school commissioner said, "did you go to Condorrumi last evening?"

Now the *comisario's* face paled. "Señor," he said, "the subprefect ordered me to go with Señor González. I did not do anything." Then he backed out and disappeared.

"You see what we are up against, Mamani. The subprefect is the supreme authority in the province."

"*Si, señor.*" Mamani and Condori both nodded.

"But, no matter what happens you can rest assured that I shall put up a good fight for your school and for the just cause of education for the people of Peru."

The *comisario* waited at the corner. The subprefect had Mamani arrested and sent with a police trooper as a prisoner to Puno.

Condori informed the school commissioner, who did not seem surprised. Then Condori went home to tell the sad story in Condorrumi.

Juana packed the burro and went with Jacinto to Puno, while Pedro Huanca somehow took care of his school, the house, and the animals. The following Sunday Condori joined Juana and Jacinto in Puno and the three visited Mamani in the jail.

"I have two *oficios* from the school commissioner." Condori showed Mamani two large envelopes, one directed to the prefect of Puno and one to the superior judge. "He also told me that he had sent telegrams both to the minister of education and to some other high-ranking official in the ministry who are his friends, as well as to authorities in Puno."

"Thank you, Condori." Mamani tried not to show how discouraged he felt. "I wish Villca would come. Please tell the missionary here in Puno."

The Ministry of Education acted promptly on Señor Cabrera's report and pressured the authorities in Puno. Condori delivered the *oficios* to the prefect and the judge, and the missionaries also

85

The Schoolhouse Burned Twice

did what they could. This time Mamani was free in two weeks.

A tired but happy family approached Condorrumi. As they turned the bend where they could first see their village, they stopped.

"Look, we are home again," Juana said, and her eyes glittered with happiness. Little Jacinto on the burro clapped his hands.

"What? What is that? What happened to our house?" Mamani could hardly believe his own eyes. What he saw was his house standing roofless with the whitewashed walls sooty and charred.

"They have burned our home!" Juana screamed, and Jacinto started to cry.

Mamani ran to the house, and Juana followed. Little Jacinto was left behind, desperately pulling on the burro, trying to make him hurry. Rubble filled the patio, and the animal corral was empty. Soon the neighbors began coming to them, and one told them what had happened.

"Many men came two nights ago. They beat Pedro Huanca almost to death. He is sick in bed at Yapo's. Then they attacked your house. They took all your sheep and the llamas and set fire to the roof. No one saw who they were, and the subprefect in Azangaro said he could not be bothered with finding out. 'Get a lawyer,' the subprefect said, 'and file a suit.' But, Mamani, I ask you, against who? You don't even know who did it."

Then another neighbor spoke up. "But in truth, Mamani, we do know who. Who would do such a thing but Señor González? I tell you, there is no justice."

Now, despite his troubles, Mamani's faith in God did not fail. He did not give up. His faith had grown strong through his experiences.

"We must go to another place," he said to Juana. "We have lost everything, but God has His plans for us. We will take Jacinto to a big school, and someday we will come back."

Pedro Huanca had not given up either. "I will take care of our school here," he said when Mamani visited him at Yapo's. "Don't worry, we will continue on the terrace, and with God's help we will have a real school next year."

He could hardly walk, but with the help of the villagers he

86

managed to be with the believers at the cave the next Sabbath. There, high over the world in the great and gorgeous heart of nature, they felt the nearness of the Creator. They sang His praise and received encouragement from His Word, the Bible. Especially Mamani felt consoled by the words of Paul, which Pedro Huanca read, "And we know that all things work together for good to them that love God."

Next day Mamani and Juana said good-bye to their neighbors. It was not easy for them, but they felt it was the best. They packed their few remaining belongings on the burro and traveled to Juliaca. There they both found work, and they registered Jacinto at the Adventist school.

Pedro Huanca successfully continued his school at the rock of the condor until a larger, better-equipped school could be established not far from Condorrumi by the help of the missionary in Llallahua and the school commissioner, Señor Cabrera.

Sergio Mamani walked out to greet the visitors. Then he pointed to the children. "This is my son Jacinto's school."

Condor Rock   12

Many years passed, and conditions in Peru changed. Condor-rumi changed also. To the casual observer, the little village would have looked the same. Humble Indian homes still clustered under the rock of the condor with scrub bushes and greenery peeking between the rocks. The same roads stretched across the pampa, though they were a little wider now, and fields of corn still filled the valley. But the people had changed, and so Condorrumi would never be the same again.

On one day flags waved from tall poles at Condorrumi. The community had a celebration, and the schoolchildren a holiday. Everyone met in the school's playground for the occasion, and the students stood by proudly dressed in school uniform, the boys in khaki pants and shirts, the girls in black skirts and crisp, white blouses.

The children kept an anxious eye on the main road until they finally saw what they had been waiting for. Two figures moved slowly toward them, and everyone knew who they were, a visiting missionary from Lima and his wife. At once the students formed into two long lines under the supervision of a teacher; and, blowing horns and beating drums, they marched out to greet their visitors. At the same time a group of village leaders led by head teacher Jacinto Mamani hurried toward the visitors to extend their welcome.

At the door of the school stood two men—Sergio Mamani, elder of the church, and Pastor Celestino Villca, director of the new Condorrumi mission station. They were surrounded by crowds of village men in their holiday best, women wearing colorful skirts, blouses, and shawls, and small children in equally bright clothing.

The Schoolhouse Burned Twice

Jacinto Mamani conducted the visitors toward the school while the pupils marched in elegant parade, which ended in a straight line in front of the school. Horns and drums still sounding, they marked time until the visitors had arrived at the door and the teacher shouted his command to halt.

Sergio Mamani walked out to greet the visitors and then looked proudly toward the school.

"Look, pastor, this is our school," he said and felt greatly moved as he pointed to the long row of handsome boys and girls standing rigidly at attention. "It is my son Jacinto's school."

The missionary smiled at Sergio Mamani as he put his arm around the Indian's shoulder and turned to admire the clean, uniformed youth. In front of the line the commanding teacher stood erect with a white baton. Next to the band a strong boy held the Peruvian banner which fluttered in the afternoon wind. "You certainly have reason to be proud."

El profesor Jacinto Mamani presented a short welcome speech. Then he told the pupils to be at ease, and the missionaries walked along the line greeting the students one by one.

Inside the schoolhouse, which also served as a church under a new roof of corrugated iron, a festive ceiling was formed by a colorful mass of small paper flags pasted to hundreds of strings stretched from wall to wall.

Villagers soon filled the hall, and the students and teachers presented a musical program in honor of the guests. Celestino Villca's wife played a small folding organ, and the congregation sang with enthusiasm. Sergio Mamani gave the opening prayer in Quechua. A series of readings, songs by the choir, and special music by a small band of horns was followed by short talks and poems. To close, a boy played violin music and another boy recited a poem dedicated to the missionary's wife.

The missionaries were invited to lunch at Villca's home, and Mamani and his family also attended. When they had finished the meal, the missionary's wife turned to Mamani.

"Tell me, Brother Mamani, how did the gospel message first come to you and to Condorrumi?"

"*Bueno*, Doña Anna. It is a long and wonderful story." Mamani

90

smiled as he remembered. "It all started in a thunderstorm, with a visit to my home of a colporteur named Celestino Villca."

The guests smiled at Pastor Villca, to whom Mamani had turned with affection. Villca's face glowed with pleasure.

"How interesting. Please tell us the whole story." Doña Anna leaned back in her chair.

Then the missionaries listened as Mamani told the whole story from Villca's visit to Condorrumi to the eventual burning of his own home.

"But what about Señor González?" the missionary asked when Mamani had finished speaking. "How did you finally get him to agree to this school?"

Mamani smiled. "Things change, and people change. We will go into that later. But now come outside and I will point out to you the rock of the condor."

"We would love to," the missionary said. "But would it be possible for us to climb up to that rock?"

"Certainly. Let us go now. We shall be glad to show you the way up there."

While Señora Villca and Juana cleared away the dinner, the others headed toward the mountain slope.

"Do you see that dark spot where the mountainside seems to be in the shadow of a great rock?" asked old Brother Mamani, as they stopped a moment for a rest. "There it is. There is where our children had their first book learning. There is where Pedro and his pupils fled after our enemies burned our school the second time. Yes, the persecution was fierce at that time."

"*Vamos,*" said the missionary. "I can't wait until I see for myself where these brave Waldenses of the Andes sought knowledge and worshiped the true God."

The climb was strenuous for the missionaries as it always is for *gringos* who are not born in the high altitude, 13,000 feet above sea level.

The little group walked across small terraced fields and *quinua* (fine-seed cereal) and *habas* (big beans) plantations. Often they had to crawl over stone fences. The higher they climbed the more beautiful became the view over the plain, the river, and the imposing mountains. The small Indian houses of Condorrumi appeared to be cozily placed in every mountain corner.

"That is the hacienda of Señor González, I suppose." Resting awhile, the missionary pointed toward the farm buildings nestled among the eucalyptus trees. "What about him? Is he still your enemy?"

"Oh, no," said Villca. "It has all changed. He is a good friend of the mission. All the ranchers are our friends now. You see, pastor, they have found that an honest, educated worker who does not drink and steal is worth much more than a drunken, lazy, coca-chewing worker.

"Not long ago Señor González asked me if I could not get him a teacher for his hacienda. He said he would build us a good schoolhouse and pay the salary if we would get him an Adventist teacher. As a deputy to the Peruvian congress, he has been a spokesman for the Indians and their defender for many years. Especially he has fought for the education of the poor of our country."

"Yes," added Mamani as they continued the climb. "One of the landowners in Santiago said to me just recently, 'If I could, I would prefer to have only Adventist workers on my hacienda. I know I can trust them.'"

Finally Mamani, who had made the ascent with the agility of a young man, announced, "So, now we are here."

"Marvelous!" exclaimed the missionary. "You could not exactly call this a cave, but it certainly is a beautiful place."

"This is the most unique schoolhouse I have ever seen," said his wife, gasping for breath and amazement. "Green floor, rock ceiling, and a tremendous big window with the most gorgeous view!"

"So this is where the first Protestants in Condorrumi had their school, where they learned to read and write, and where amidst persecution they came together to worship God." The missionary bowed his head in reverent admiration. Then he looked down over the plain and up into the blue sky.

"Yes, pastor, here we had our divine services, and here we prayed to God," said Mamani, "and here God heard our prayers."

"But the ruins of the twice-burned schoolhouse still stands there." The missionary nodded toward the ruins.

"Yes, pastor, that is true," Mamani smiled. "But look to your left and you will see that God answered our prayers."

There at the foot of the mountain about a quarter of a mile from the old school building stood the new well-built mission station, glorious in the sunshine with its shining roof of corrugated iron. A neat whitewashed building stood next to the school—the mission director's home. A patio with straw-topped walls surrounded the two buildings. What a glorious testimony these faithful believers had borne to the power of the gospel.

"Thanks be to God. It is marvelous!" the missionary finally said. "He has blessed so much. But do you know, Mamani, what is still more wonderful is that there are many schools like this one. If we could climb much higher, and if our eyes were much stronger, we could see at least a hundred more schools on the Peruvian highland stretching before us, and on the far side of Lake Titicaca in Bolivia we could see some 200 more. Yes, about 11,000 children and young Indians receive their primary education in these 300 schools." The missionary stretched out his hand and pointed from one end of the horizon to the other.

"Thanks to God for the hundreds of faithful teachers like Jacinto and Pedro who have gone out from our Juliaca training school and from our superior school in Cochabamba in Bolivia. They are not just schoolteachers, but also evangelists teaching the people the word of the Lord. Every year hundreds of precious souls are baptized as a result of the work of these teachers. Today we have over 17,000 baptized Seventh-day Adventists among the Quechua and Aymara Indians."

"Pastor," said Mamani, "shall we not pray together and thank the Lord?"

With a strange sense of reverence the four knelt down—the old village leader, the Indian mission-station director, and the foreign missionary with his wife. They knelt together in the lofty mountain tabernacle to praise and thank God for His love and for what the gospel had accomplished in the hearts of these Indian people of the Andean highlands.